DUTCH DRAWINGS FROM THE COLLECTION OF
DR C. HOFSTEDE DE GROOT

GRONINGER MUSEUM VOOR STAD EN LANDE

DUTCH DRAWINGS

from the Collection of
Dr C. Hofstede de Groot

AN INTRODUCTION AND CRITICAL CATALOGUE BY

J. BOLTEN

1967

A. OOSTHOEK'S UITGEVERSMAATSCHAPPIJ N.V.

UTRECHT

DISTRIBUTED BY NEW YORK GRAPHIC SOCIETY LTD.

GREENWICH / CONNECTICUT

The photographs have been made by P. Boonstra, Groningen;
the colour positives by P. D. van der Poel, Amsterdam.
Printed in The Netherlands by Joh. Enschedé en Zonen
Grafische Inrichting N.V., Haarlem.

TABLE OF CONTENTS

LIST OF ILLUSTRATIONS

The Plates

8

Text Illustrations

9

PREFACE

The collection of drawings bequeathed to the city of Groningen by Hofstede de Groot has never been exhaustively studied or published in full. Hitherto, the only source of reference has been a small booklet containing brief entries, which was published on the occasion of an exhibition held in the Groningen Museum in 1931. Since that time, individual items from the collection have occasionally been discussed in articles, monographs and exhibition catalogues.

It is hoped that the present catalogue will serve several purposes. Firstly, that of recapitulating previous comments on the various drawings, in so far as this seems deserving of attention. Secondly, of assembling all available data regarding technique and provenance. Thirdly, of reconsidering the traditional attributions in the light of our present-day knowledge in matters of art history. Fourthly, of bringing to the notice of the general public a rich treasure which is theirs to enjoy. Lastly, since the remarkable paucity of detailed catalogues of important Dutch collections of drawings is a matter of regret both to the interested layman and more especially to the student and connoisseur, the most important function of the publication will be to supplement the scholarly literature in this particular field of art history, in which a great deal of work remains to be done.

Since the catalogue is the result of our personal efforts, certain aspects of it will reflect—we hope and trust to the credit of that institution—the training received at the Institute of the History of Art at Groningen University. We wish to express our special gratitude to Professor H. Schulte Nordholt, to whose teaching and encouragement, above all, we feel indebted for our understanding of art. Other scholars and friends to whom we are also indebted are too numerous to mention here. However, we must ask Professor J. Q. van Regteren Altena to accept our sincere thanks for his generosity in allowing us to profit from his erudition and connoisseurship. Professor J. G. van Gelder, Professor H. van de Waal and Mr. Frits Lugt have given us generous help, lending a patient ear during the course of this investigation, giving valuable information and guidance. Professor E. K. J. Reznicek has given us much stimulus and help in conversation.

Our thanks are also due to the officials of the Printroom of the Rijksmuseum, Amsterdam, The Rijksbureau voor Kunsthistorische Documentatie, The Hague, and the Institute of the History of Art, Groningen, who allowed us to use the *apparatus criticus* at their disposal.

The English manuscript was corrected by Mrs. F. M. Daendels-Wilson, thus gaining in style and fluency. Thanks to the active interest of the publisher, Mr. L. Bunge, the form and appearance of this catalogue do justice to its subject.

With gratitude, we acknowledge that the research required for this catalogue was made possible through a grant from the Groningen University Fund.

INTRODUCTION

In the text of this critical catalogue, we have followed throughout an arrangement of the entries into two parts: under each item is given, firstly, the fullest possible factual information, arranged in strictly uniform grouping in order to facilitate quick reference; and secondly, a discussion of the drawing, which may be quite brief or more extended, depending on the facts established. The discussions could not be treated formally, since each item required an individual approach, and a strictly schematic arrangement was found to be unsatisfactory. We believe that the reader will find a freer treatment more stimulating. To the best of our ability we have aimed at clear and simple statement.

Names of artists are given in their Dutch spelling, as is customary. The titles of the drawings have been kept as short as possible, but care has been taken to avoid any possibility of confusion with other drawings in the collection by the same artist. Data concerning technique, size, inscriptions, watermarks and owner's marks have been grouped together. In giving measurements, the height is given first, followed by the width. Watermarks are reproduced on page 245 in this catalogue. With regard to owner's marks, the name of the owner of the collection is given; for biographical particulars of these collectors, we refer to the numbered series in F. Lugt's *Les marques de collections,* where the reader will find a wealth of supplementary data of cultural-historical value. The bibliography of the various drawings also requires explanation: publications directly mentioning or reproducing any of the drawings from the collection are listed in the first part of the entry which contains the data, the author's name being followed by the year of publication. In the bibliography, these names are repeated in alphabetical order with the title given in full; books or articles referred to in the course of the text are, however, not included in the general bibliography but are quoted in full in a footnote. In every case where a reproduction of a drawing exists, this has been indicated by an asterisk (*). Since completeness has been aimed at, publications of possibly minor importance have been included.

The various exhibitions are also noted as fully as possible; doubtful cases have been indicated by a question-mark.

In general, very little is known about the provenance of the drawings. Apparently, Hofstede de Groot was not interested very much in the pedigree of his possessions. The original inventory of his collection, now at the Rijksbureau voor Kunsthistorische Documentatie at The Hague, mentions only the auction or the name of the art dealer from whom the drawing was acquired. It has been impossible to establish a complete pedigree for the majority of the drawings. That we were able to trace a number of previous owners is due for the most part to F. Lugt's two excellent and indispensable standard works. The numbered items in *Répertoire des catalogues de ventes publiques* have been indicated by (L...), as distinct from those taken from *Les marques de collections* which are indicated by (Lugt...). We know that some drawings certainly belonged to particular collections as indicated by the owner's mark. When such a drawing could not be traced in the catalogues of the relevant sale (in many of these catalogues the entries are brief or incomplete), only the name of the collection has been mentioned. When two consecutive collections could be found, this is indicated by a dash (—). The texts to the drawings contain a number of auxiliary illustrations and references to the literature. When the source of an information is given by a person's name only, this always means that the information was communicated personally, either orally or in writing.

In discussing the drawings, the first aim has been to compare them to other works by the same artist, preferably to documented drawings. This comparison proved very useful in most cases, since in this way many facts could be deduced concerning authenticity, chronology and importance. By using this comparative method, it becomes possible to write positively about a work of art. Making use of all the possibilities of factual knowledge, we may sometimes arrive at a deeper understanding. For it is often the underlying hint of a person or of a period which would really satisfy our curiosity. To illustrate this point it may be useful to consider the portraits. They represent a relatively large part of the collection, 17 of the 115 drawings, so that we have a wide field of comparison; of these 17 portraits, 6 had been previously identified (nos. 4, 5, 37, 45, 46 and 57), 3 of these wrongly (nos. 4, 5 and 45). We have corrected the errors and have made 9 new identifications (nos. 4, 5, 25, 38, 39, 45, 50, 98 and 99). These technical preliminaries seem trivial, however, when compared with the wealth of historical and human documents that pile up in front of the student. Seen side by side, the portrait of Cumberland by De Gheyn (no. 25) and Rembrandt's drawing of Saskia (no. 57) reveal two totally different worlds, yet in time they are only thirty-five years apart. The clue to this difference lies in the appreciation of the fact that Rembrandt's utter disregard of style is in complete contrast to the traditional conception of the late mannerist. Yet both artists reveal their true natures, the one thanks to his lack of style and the other just because of his special manner. Another example in favour of the assertion that a true and justifiable appreciation should be supported by factual evidence can be found in two landscape drawings, both listed under Lievens' name. When we compare the landscape with the windmill (no. 47) with the landscape with the little bridge (no. 48), and assert that the former is superior, this is not merely a figment of the imagination once we know that the latter is indeed a copy of the original drawing in another collection.

Rembrandt's landscape with the roller-bridge (no. 69) contains an element which goes beyond our mere observation of the undoubted likeness with other views of the same spot, however interesting the comparisons may be in themselves. The comparisons may also serve to make us realise the way in which Rembrandt uses the scene, rebuilds and modifies it into a unique and personal vision, and then only do the implications become wholly comprehensible.

Unfortunately, there are enormous gaps in our factual knowledge concerning many of the drawings. Where there is no historical starting-point on which a deeper understanding can be based, we are forced to make use of the experience we have acquired in dealing with more favourable cases. In studying the Rembrandt drawings, especially, we were often confronted with the difficulty of deciding on their authenticity. In general, we share Benesch's views, but there were a few instances where we were reluctantly forced to disagree. W. Sumowski[1] touches upon the difficulties of this kind: 'Das Ideal einer vollständigen Ausgabe der Rembrandtzeichnungen wird, durch den problematischen Charakter der Kritik bedingt, niemals Wirklichkeit werden. Es gibt nur wenige völlig gesicherte Blätter des Meisters innerhalb einer Flut rembrandtesken Materials, und jeder Forscher, der sich um das zeichnerische Oeuvre Rembrandts bemüht, bildet sich am einwandfreien Werkbestand subjektive Auswahlprinzipien und vollzieht dann eine individuelle Auslese. Das Ergebnis, das Corpus, kann daher stets nur

[1] Werner Sumowski, 'Rembrandt Zeichnungen', in *Pantheon* XXII, 4, Juli/August, 1964, p. 233.

ein Ordnungssystem darstellen, das, von der Zuschreibung der einzelnen Zeichnung bis zu den Dimensionen des angeblichen Gesamtwerks, die kritischen Überzeugungen seines Urhebers wiederspiegelt. So erklären sich die Unterschiede zwischen den Publikationen von Hofstede de Groot, Valentiner und Benesch.'

This resignation, wise and sensible though it may be, does not necessarily have to be our last resort. It should be realized that we stand only at the beginning of what we hope will be an evergrowing chain of Rembrandt corpora. Surely, after the combined efforts of several generations of scholars, a more reliable approach to his work will emerge.

It may be of interest to give a brief appraisal of the collection. Although the bequest to Groningen was only a part of the collection, yet it may be taken as representative of the quality of the whole; the contents of the Boerner sale in 1931 and the bequest to the Rijksprentenkabinet in Amsterdam do not differ from it essentially. Although we find several drawings of the highest quality, the selection itself is not outstanding; the choice, one would have thought, of a connoisseur rather than an art historian. Indeed these two types of art expert were not as different then as they are nowadays, the aims of the two having grown far apart. When the collection was formed, in the two or three decades around the turn of the century, the study of the history of art in Holland was only in its first stages, dealing almost exclusively with factual, or at its best, stylistic problems. Far be it from us to detract from the reputation of the diligent compilers of those days, yet it may be useful to see Hofstede de Groot in the context of his time in order to reach a fair appreciation. In Holland, as elsewhere, there had always been a strong tradition of great collectors of drawings. Their kind of knowledge, of connoisseurship with a training in the discernment of style and quality, was to a large extent the basis of De Groot's collecting and study, as indicated by his later activities and publications. We must not forget that the study of art in the Netherlands and again elsewhere, has its roots in the non-professional avocations of the collector, in the commercial attitude of the art dealer and the disinterested occupation of gentlemen of leisure who became keepers of museums in order to pass their time.

Gradually a number of new elements, without exception originating abroad, enriched the study of the history of art. De Groot, in his younger days, could already have been cognizant of some of the best thinking in this field. One is tempted to wonder how his collection and publications would have looked had he been influenced in his student years by one of the great art historians of the time.

Dr H. E. van Gelder's brilliant biography of De Groot[1] shows us that he was not a particularly happy man and that he often came into conflict with his contemporaries; countless were the clashes with museum officials and government authorities. These controversies, however, were not prompted by a protest against art historical methods but were due to his particular cast of mind. Significant is the handwritten complaint on the fly-leaf of the catalogue of an exhibition[2] for which De Groot apparently had done a good deal of the work: 'Out of the 124 paintings exhibited, over 90 were obtained as a result of my investigation, through my intervention or on my advice. I spent ca. 120 guldens for postage fees, compiled the catalogue, edited the commemorative volume, travelled to England (three times) and South Germany.

[1] The board of Directors of the Maatschappij der Nederlandsche Letterkunde, Leiden, kindly permitted us to include this biography; an English translation follows this introduction.

[2] Amsterdam, Municipal Museum, Rembrandt exhibition, 1898; this copy of the catalogue can be consulted at the Rijksbureau voor Kunsthistorische Documentatie, The Hague.

I proposed the nomination of the foreign members of honour, was instrumental in obtaining the paintings of the Queen of England and of the city of Amsterdam; I asked the Queen to visit the exhibition a second time, got the art history congress to Amsterdam, and worked for half a year almost exclusively for the exhibition, but *nobody,* neither the government nor the committee of principal inhabitants, nor the society 'Arti', nor the Chairman of the Rembrandt committee gave me even the *slightest word of thanks.* If it comes to that, the gentlemen of the Royal Academy, for which I did far less, were quite different! C. H. de G.'

However justified this invective in itself might have been, we seem to detect the voice of a man grown accustomed to defending himself against unjust treatment and who, by no means surprisingly, repeatedly lands himself in a similar situation. Moreover, the reproach that somewhere else things are done better fits perfectly into the picture of a man living in discord with his surroundings.

Notwithstanding frequent friction, De Groot never isolated himself from the scientific approach of his colleagues. By working extremely hard, he tried to overtrump them by discovering yet another small master or lost painting in some forgotten archive or museum. Had De Groot studied in Basle or Vienna, he might have been moved to curiosity about the connection between facts, instead of his inquisitiveness for single facts. As it was, he has added to the history of art the fruits of his incessant and zealous work, but without noticeably altering its course. In the collection we are reminded of De Groot's encyclopaedic tendencies. Concentrated as it is upon the Dutch seventeenth century, everything within this field was welcome if the quality fulfilled the requirements of certain standards. Thanks to his early and justified appreciation of the drawings of the Dutch masters, we are now the heirs of some precious documents. And also thanks to Hofstede de Groot, a large number of the best of Rembrandt's drawings has been preserved for The Netherlands (the Printroom at Amsterdam has also benifited by his collecting fervour).

We sincerely hope that the present publication will have served its purpose, that of revealing the treasure entrusted to us and of imparting the results of our study to whoever may be interested.

In the *Proceedings* of the Maatschappij der Nederlandsche Letterkunde, Leiden, 1931, pp. 99–125, Dr H. E. van Gelder published a biography of Dr Cornelis Hofstede de Groot, followed by a bibliography compiled by Dr H. Gerson. By kind permission of Professor Dr J. G. van Gelder and of the Board of Directors of the Maatschappij der Nederlandsche Letterkunde, we include an English translation by Mrs. F. M. Daendels-Wilson of this obituary notice of Hofstede de Groot by a contemporary, which contains a remarkably profound and sincere appraisal of his life, work and character.

DR C. HOFSTEDE DE GROOT

(1863–1930)

Schweizerhof, Interlaken, August 1929. On the verandah, my wife and I are De Groot's guests. He has chosen the meal with great care, he assures us that a certain wine will meet with our approval, he gives his orders with the confidence of the regular visitor, he does the honours of the house and surroundings, which for us are mainly new, and all with the almost exaggerated courtesy of an earlier generation, often the mark of the bachelor, exerting himself for our comfort as he would not think of doing for his own in the ordinary way. He tells my wife about the holidays he has spent here for so many years, how he had this year stayed first in Gunten, where his sister and an old friend of the family were his guests. Otherwise they would not have been able to permit themselves such a stay, and he wanted them once again to enjoy the memories of the Beatenberg of more than a half-century ago, when both ladies were there with him on account of his ill-health. And for a little while he relives those bygone days ... I only half-listened: my thoughts went back to the thin, half-grown boy, with the frail look—I had once seen a photograph of him taken during his student days—and compared it with the man, already old, who sat opposite me. It was all so different from the first time I had met him, twenty-five years before when I joined the Historical Society of The Hague, shortly after my arrival there! Now, with the white hair growing long on his neck, the skin of his face yellowish, flabby and relaxed, and the heavily veined hand nervously crumbling and re-crumbling a roll of bread: for a moment, I saw before me the figure of the typical German professor as in one of Thoma's or Gulbransson's somewhat mischievous caricatures.

Yes, you always had something of that German professor about you, De Groot. Even twenty-five years ago, when I visited you in the somewhat cheerless, overcrowded study at no. 5 Heerengracht, where the big cupboard containing your reproductions filled a whole wall; every available space full of books, photographs and other work material, the jutting walls crammed with paintings; you yourself, sitting at the old-fashioned roll-top desk, hard at work, resilient, unwearied, continually busy, helpful, counseling, arguing in that typical clipped accent of your native city, seeming to smother contradiction before it was even made. Your star was still in the ascendant, the 'Privatgelehrte', who had carved his own way to international fame; consulted far and wide, a regular traveller on international expresses which carried you to all the corners of Europe where your opinions on Dutch art were sought. Between whiles, calmly and systematically, with the help of your assistants you were preparing the book which was to become your standard work.

As a result of the strenuous life of a profession which continuously demanded all your mental and physical energy you were old and worn out before your time. But I did not think at that time that a collapse would come so soon, scarcely a year after this Swiss holiday. It came as a shock to everyone, even to those near and dear to De Groot, although they had observed with alarm his weary look, his increasingly bowed back and difficulty in walking. To think of De Groot was to think of work, of action, of anything rather than rest, let alone rest for ever. Which of us who saw him more or less regularly in his own surroundings does not still have some vivid recollection of a discussion, an appointment, a consultation, or of planning

Max Liebermann, *Portrait of Dr C. Hofstede de Groot*, etching

to meet him on one of those rare free days in his diary of engagements, a diary which was always fully booked for weeks ahead? But if we think back, the suspicion arises that he must have felt in later years that it could not go on for much longer. He spoke to his friends often about finishing things, completing this or that. This compulsion asked too much of his body, apparently strong but in reality frail, and gradually it destroyed his reserves of strength. Allowing himself less and less rest at a time when he needed more and more, he went on burning himself out up until the last moment. And as often seems to happen with this type of man, he fell in the midst of his work, 'in harness' and 'with the honours of the warrior'.

Cornelis Hofstede de Groot was born on 9 November 1863, at Dwingeloo, the eldest son of Cornelis Philippus Hofstede de Groot, doctorandus (master of arts), and Catharina Dorothea Star Numan, both citizens of Groningen and themselves the children of professors. Grandfather Hofstede de Groot, in a long and fruitful career as a professor of Theology, had won himself a special place in the Dutch theological world as the militant leader of the so-called 'Groningen School'. 'He was one of those people, who fiercely assert their opinions, who can hardly imagine that anyone else of good faith could not agree with him ... capable of great courage, given to the greatest inconsistencies and self-deception.' Grandfather Star Numan was a devoted disciple of Van Heusden, the same Utrecht philosopher who so greatly influenced De Groot's theology. He lacked De Groot's sharply defined militancy, but surpassed him certainly in his ardour as a teacher. In spite of his fiery religious convictions, he had a strong antipathy to systems and factions, so that there remains something vague in the picture of his spiritual life; it is closely akin to the rather nebulous idealism, the enthusiasms of heart and mind, of his mentor Van Heusden, whose 'softness' was so displeasing to such contemporaries as Thorbecke, Geel and Cobet.

In spite of the confusion which sometimes marked his lectures, Star Numan was a well-loved teacher, and many people benefited from his erudition and his well-stocked library. He had a fine mind, and when he died suddenly in 1857, he was forgotten all too quickly.[1]

De Groot had certain characteristic qualities in common with both his grandfathers. He inherited the capacity for hard work from both, but certainly the qualities of leadership and perseverance came from his father's side. His interest in the Arts came indeed from the Numans, not in the first place from the grandfather, but from the grandmother. Jonkvrouwe van Swinderen was a real Groningen woman, one of the most cultured and highly respected women of her day and withal a genuine art connoisseur. The influence of De Groot's father and mother was less important than that of the older generation.[2]

Cornelis' earliest memories of his parents' house were of the manse in Kampen.

The life of a minister of the Church was frequently uncomfortable; with a family that grew quickly in a few years, in the narrow circle of a conservative city, the father was often depressed, for he had something of the passion for action of the Groningen professor in him, but without his cheerful character; it was a life which often cost De Groot's mother, a more delicate creature, more of her strength than her nerves could afford. Thus there may have been sometimes a lack of stability and direction in the life of the family which could not fail to exert an influence on Cornelis' mentality, for like his grandfather he was very impression-

---

[1] On these characteristics, see Huizinga in the 'Jubilee Book' of the Groningen Academy.

[2] The influence of his artistic aunt (his mother's sister), hereafter called 'Aunt Anne Willem Star Numan', was also of great importance.

able. These conditions produced a youth of serious and reflective temperament, a tendency already present in the boy, who was precocious, greedy for knowledge, and burdened with a weak constitution. In the childish games with his sisters and the boys and girls in their circle of friends, he was the master and liked even more to play the role of pastor. The maxims in his small diary and the quotations in his letters are all devout in sentiment, certainly not at all strange in one belonging to a minister's family.

The family's move to the university city of Groningen, where his father was appointed to a Chair in 1878, could have led to a rather more relaxed manner of living. On the one hand, connections through the Star Numans with the Van Swinderens and through them with the circle of the leading landed gentry of the country, and, on the other hand, the normal contact with families of professors of other faculties, might have eased the pressure at home and also dissipated the oppressive atmosphere af a small town, but the young professor's unexpected death, only six years after his inauguration, left his bereaved family in severe difficulties.

Cornelis' youth, in the mean time, among a troop of brothers and sisters deeply attached to one another, had not lasted long. In the autumn of 1874, he suffered a severe attack of bronchitis and because most serious complications were feared, he was taken by his grandmother Star Numan to Arcachon, along with her daughter, Anna, who had to undergo a cure for a lung complaint.

This was his first trip abroad and everything he saw and experienced made a deep impression on him—among other places, they visited Paris and the Louvre.

In September, 1876, he began school at the Gymnasium (grammar school) in Kampen. In May, 1878, after the move to Groningen, he went to the Gymnasium there, but in 1880 he had to go south again because of his weak lungs. With his eldest sister and in the care of the same aunt, he travelled up the Rhine and through Switzerland, where they stayed for quite a long time on the Beatenberg,[1] ending up in Arcachon where De Groot became a pupil at the Gymnasium at St. Elme. It was a year of special importance for his education. His contact with French and English fellow pupils, the greater measure of independance in his work, his catechism under the Protestant minister, by whom he was confirmed in the spring of 1881: all these things brought an early maturity to the gifted boy. This stood him in good stead when he returned to Groningen, when it appeared that it was inadvisable for him to go back to the Gymnasium, since an outdoor life was indicated and not one of study. A training for market-gardening or forestry seemed to be the best choice, but eventually it was decided to send him to live with the family Rückert on their estate at Neuses, situated a half-hour's journey from Coburg, and thus he attended the Gymnasium there. In this way, he had both an outdoor life and study at the same time.

This stay at Neuses satisfied his already curious mind, for here the milieu attracted him and he had daily contact with Germans of a high intellectual standard. Moreover, long walks in the interesting surrounding country, where there was a great deal of historical and art-historical material, stimulated his fast growing and deep interest, and this gave a firm direction to his life.[2] On a visit to Bamberg, for example, he decided to make a close study of the Dom,

[1] This was the holiday which he remembered with so much pleasure in the summer of 1929.

[2] As early as 1883, he had corresponded with his Aunt Anne about his study in this field. In a remarkable letter (Nov. 1883) she gives her objections to it and she poses the problem: 'not that I wish to discourage you, but to place before you right at the beginning the wise point of view ... I do not know what inner forces you have to give to the world, in other words, how much originality you possess.'

and in so doing he discovered several inaccuracies in Baedeker's description. This gave him the opportunity to initiate a correspondence with the publisher. So even from this period he began to collaborate in the compilation of guide books, a work which lasted practically all his life. One Easter holiday he stayed with a fellow scholar in Neurenberg, and yet another holiday took him to München; from there he sent his first articles to the *Nieuwe Rotterdamsche Courant*. This was also to be a life-long connection. The honorarium for this work made it possible to extend the journey to the Tirol. When travelling to and from Groningen he always took a different route, and by practising the strictest economies he was able to continue his studies in art history: Hildesheim, Brunswick, Cassel were visited in this way. He travelled as cheaply as possible, slept overnight at railway stations and lived on bread. During the visit to München, mentioned above, it had become quite clear to him that Art History was the subject he wished to study, and in spite of the objections that everyone at home had against it, he applied himself even more energetically. The moment he had passed his final examinations in Coburg, he left directly for Leipzig, where he placed himself under the tutelage of Springer. The future, however, was to be quite different. At the end of July, 1884, Professor Hofstede de Groot had a serious stroke, and at the beginning of August the end came: the son had to go home, and the possibility of studying in Germany in a subject that had so little future was ruled out. The financial troubles of the bereaved family were enormous. They were completely dependent on Grandmother Star Numan, with her very decided views regarding 'suitable' economy. Cornelis was forced to fit himself as quickly as possible for a position. He changed over to study Classics.

The life of the student had many pleasures even for the poor son of a professor, but his seriousness was still predominant. His fellow students found him rather pedantic; the older ones saw what good stuff there was in him, while he often gave real support to the younger ones. Work was, nevertheless, the important thing, but it did not satisfy him: Halbertsma's ideas, in his opinion, lagged behind those of the German classical scholars, and moreover, in spite of hard work, he could not keep up his arthistory studies, which he still thought necessary. In the end, he arranged to be transferred to Leiden, where Hartman coached him and where he took his 'candidaats' (bachelor of arts) degree.

The failure in Groningen was due not only to the difference of opinion with Halbertsma, but more to a general crisis, in the course of which he worked out what was to be his life's goal. He would not give up Art History because he was drawn to it with all his heart and soul. But the cost he had to pay was high. Not only had he to fight the prudent members of the family, who disapproved of a study which had so little future, but he had also to struggle with himself. He realized that this choice could prevent his asking the young German girl, with whom he had fallen in love, to share the uncertainty which awaited him. When once the choice of the profession had been made, then according to the stern voice of duty, his unspoken love had to remain unspoken. Eventually, with the help of uncle Star Numan, who had been convinced by the perseverance, industry and earnestness of his nephew,[1] the grandmother's resistance was broken. In 1889, eight hundred guldens were set aside for one year's study in Leipzig. The most stringent economy was therefore demanded; De Groot tried to earn extra money by writing for the *Nieuwe Rotterdamsche Courant* and other papers; he sold his stamp collection, economized on his food, came home thin and starving. But he brought a consolation prize with him, his appointment as temporary assistant at the Printroom

[1] In a very detailed and interesting letter, dated 7 August, 1889.

in Dresden, where he started work on 20 October, 1890. 1500 Marks 'Jahresgehalt'! It was not much, but it was a beginning. Moreover, it was laid before his Dutch family as evidence that the profession could lead to a regular 'job'. Yet, even so, he had hesitated: he wanted to be sure that he would not have to give up his Dutch nationality. In Leipzig, he met Woermann, Max Lehrs (with whom he became very friendly) and Von Seidlitz; their companionship, friendliness and above all their mutual scholarly interests meant very much to him. Remarkably enough, originally it was architecture that particularly attracted De Groot; his wanderings and journeys were concerned with that and with archeology,[1] with which he had been brought into contact by his classical studies. The museums were not neglected either; De Groot's thirst for knowledge saw to that, as well as his desire to exploit to the full those journeys which had only been made possible by much sacrifice and effort. During his time in Leipzig, he came to realise the desirability of specialising in another direction, and this decision had already been taken even before the choice of subject for his thesis. An outside influence had played a role here, namely the line of thought suggested by a highly respected Dutch colleague, A. Bredius, a man deeply revered by De Groot.

De Groot had come into contact with Bredius before his departure for Dresden, although it was only a superficial acquaintance; during his stay there, they exchanged letters leading to a closer friendship. Encouraged by Bredius, he determined to make a special study of the art of Dutch painting in the seventeenth century. The subject suited De Groot's character, for his heart went out to his native land above all. Over and over again in his letters there is evidence of how he feels the necessity to serve Dutch interests. To be able to do this in the subject that he loved could only be more than welcome to him. His treatise on Houbraken's importance for the knowledge of the Dutch school of painting, the thesis written for his Leipzig doctorate, brought him into the middle of that specialized field.

It would be difficult to exaggerate the impact of De Groot's personality and work in Leipzig and Dresden, his industry, his connections with everyone who was interested in the same subject. His manner of working, his rapid accumulation of great factual knowledge, his sharp powers of observation and his unflagging energy were an inspiration to many. At this early date, he was commissioned to compile the catalogue of the 'Sammlung Schubart' in München (which was to appear in 1894); there was also his regular collaboration with the *Nieuwe Rotterdamsche Courant*; also his close contact with Baedeker, under whose aegis a little later, in 1893, he made his first journey to England, where in one month he visited no less than twenty-four private collections, and revised this material for a new edition of the guide-book. That this was not the only work done is shown by his bibliography. In Dresden, while studying a painting signed 'Janssens', he came on the track of the De Hoogh pupil, P. Janssens Elinga, to whom he also ascribed the De Hooghs in München and Frankfurt. He reaped the reward of success when he laid these opinions before Bode and Bredius; they both accepted them immediately. Bredius wrote with great warmth to him about it. He did more. Shortly afterwards, he asked De Groot to come and work with him at the Mauritshuis; this opportunity was seized with

[1] He always kept up this interest. After the war, when negotiations between the Government and Professor Von Bissing concerning a professorship had failed, and thus the chance of acquiring his collection of Egyptian Art for the country was lost, it was De Groot who discussed the matter with Dr Lunsingh Scheurleer, with the result that Professor Von Bissing was appointed Professor in Utrecht at the instance of the *Haagsche Academie voor Beeldende Kunsten*, and that his collection came to The Netherlands. The *Academie* appointed Hofstede de Groot as Curator of this Chair. This is again evidence of the fact that his interests were more varied than many thought.

both hands and at the beginning of August, 1891, De Groot took up his appointment as assistant director, remaining there as such until November, 1896.

The collaboration of these two extraordinary men, lasting for five years, was of quite exceptional importance in the development of Dutch art history. Both possessed an equally great love for the art of old Dutch painting, a devotion to their work, resulting quite naturally in the surrender of their total personality. Each was a wonderful complement to the other. De Groot's letters home witness great admiration for Bredius' knowledge, taste, perspicuity and balanced outlook. For De Groot, this period is above all still an apprenticeship; a period of evolving a method, and accumulating a rich store of material. He saw much and travelled widely, sometimes under orders, sometimes at Bredius' invitation, going among other places to Spain, and profited from the lively connections that Bredius maintained personally and by letter with all those, inside and outside our frontiers, interested in problems arising from the study of the old art of our fatherland.

Bredius and he complemented each other, certainly, not only by what they had in common but also by their differences.

These differences caused them to part in later years, and must inevitably have caused such a parting, however regrettable for the science which they both served with devotion and conviction. There was in any case a difference in talent and character, and, in order to understand De Groot, it is necessary to sketch here the contrast which played such a role in his life.

De Groot was, and was to remain throughout his life, a spiritual child of the nineteenth century, with its faith in Science. Facts and proved experiment were prized by him above everything else. If one reads his book *Art and knowledge of art* written towards the end of his life, one finds that he confirms this himself: a work of art is there considered as a construction the same as any other; the scientist assesses its composition and characteristics without emotion or prejudice. It is just a piece of arithmetic.

As the letters in which he pleaded the cause of his profession to his uncle Star Numan bear witness, De Groot knew, of course, that the subject-matter of these scientific researches was the end-product of the mental processes of exceptionally talented and varied types of people, and he had undoubtedly also derived great pleasure from art. He sincerely admired beautiful colour, perfect drawing, fine execution, and rich composition, and because of his great knowledge and practised eye he could indicate these things and explain them clearly to others.

But he never experienced the subtle ecstasy, the intoxication of the spirit intensely felt by the creative artist, nor believed in the scientist's intuition. As he got older, he became, as it were, more and more the prisoner of his own method, isolated from these integral elements of art, an isolation that increased rather than lessened. Especially to those who had lacked the opportunity of close personal contact with him, whereby the seriousness of his aesthetic perception could be appreciated, De Groot came to be regarded more and more as the clever arithmetician.

Bredius was different. He applied, in principle, the same scientific methods, but less systematically, without the card-index mind. He retained a suppleness, and, as he was a passionate musician, he was able to enter into the artist's inner experiences. Thus, eventually, De Groot could not stand what he called Bredius' 'dilettantism', although he appreciated him greatly, and Bredius was irritated by the 'schoolmaster' in De Groot. There was, in fact, a deep unbridgeable gulf between the rich, young man of good family and the poor, puritanical minister's son with his Groningen stiffness. A partnership was possible only during the first rapture of working together on important work; otherwise they were incompatible.

Yet, that first burst of work had indeed produced much that was good. The study of Dutch painting was advanced by the findings resulting from a sifting and searching in many collections, most of which appeared in *Oud Holland*, providing material for the series of articles which appeared as *Quellenstudiën zur holländischen Kunstgeschichte,* initiated and edited by De Groot, which opened with an expansion of his thesis about Houbraken's *'Groote Schouburgh'*; and by the many expert opinions given on purchases and restorations. The Mauritshuis itself also benefited. As Bredius' collaborator, De Groot compiled the catalogue and organized the library. The result of the eminent direction of these two fine experts in Dutch painting was that the Museum acquired the leading position which it has retained. What the Rijksmuseum lacked in this period and lacked for many years, this small and easily accessible museum possessed in abundance, and that gave it an even greater advantage.

The collaboration lasted only a few years. In 1895, De Groot was approached by Philip van der Kellen, Director of the Rijks Prentenkabinet in Amsterdam, as to whether he would consider being his successor. De Groot did not hesitate: this was just what he wanted and it was, moreover, a position for life. Not that he put security before everything else. Had he not a short time before refused a much better offer, namely a highly-paid appointment to travel and buy for a big London antique dealer? What attracted him to the Amsterdam proposition? There was work to be done at the Print Room; it had rich possessions which had been judiciously expanded by Van der Kellen, a distinguished authority in his field. But Van der Kellen had neither a bent for organisation nor the slightest interest in the general public. The stories which circulated about his way of doing things bordered on the incredible.[1] It was an attractive programme for De Groot to reorganise the collection and to fill in the deficiencies. Moreover, the idea that Van der Kellen himself wished him to be his successor,[2] opened up the prospect of a collaboration profitable to the collection, of which De Groot had great hopes, quite apart from increasing his own knowledge.

The result was quite different. De Groot's two years as director brought him practically nothing but unpleasantness. It is not easy to form an opinion about what happened; we know only what the parties concerned tell us.[3] If I judge rightly, De Groot made the tactical mistake of showing too much zeal when he began to reorganize the kabinet, which was by consensus of opinion 'a dreadful mess', and he thereby irritated Van der Kellen, who was, in any case, suffering from severe nervous afflictions. Van der Kellen transformed his original collaboration into active opposition and found a willing listener in Victor de Stuers,[4] whose character had very little in common with that of De Groot. De Groot had to begin very early on, defending his position as director tooth and nail against the interference of the all-powerful referendary. Those who knew De Groot and De Stuers can imagine the conflicts and also the unedifying manner in which they were fought out. On De Groot's side it was a continual effort to escape the clutches of the director, sometimes by means of somewhat far-fetched equivocation. One example from many: De Stuers arranged that drawings which were coming up for auction in Amsterdam should be sent to The Hague. There, with Van der Kellen, he

[1] We give one example: during an International Art History Conference held in Amsterdam, Van der Kellen closed the Kabinet to all visitors.

[2] In fact, Van der Kellen's attitude was extremely equivocal: at the last moment he supported another candidate, but De Groot knew nothing of this.

[3] See De Groot's pamphlet: *My directorship of the Rijks Prentenkabinet.*

[4] Hofstede de Groot's appointment was made against the advice of the referendary; De Stuers was on sick leave.

selected what he thought was of importance for the Prentenkabinet, gave a commission to a third party to buy at the sale, and instructed De Groot that he was not to bid for those numbers in his own name. It can be appreciated that De Groot found these methods incompatible with the professional responsibilities that he had taken upon himself. When his protest had no effect in this and similar cases, he applied first to Minister van Houten, asking him to define the respective responsibilities of the Director and his Head Assistant. When the Minister declined to make any alteration in the De Stuers régime, De Groot decided to resign. Current political circumstances made the resignation of Minister Van Houten most probable, and De Groot delayed his decision, hoping that Van Houten's successor would see the case in another light. But when Minister Goeman Borgesius supported the referendary, De Groot applied for an honourable discharge from his office, effective from 1 July 1898.

He thought that now this difficult period was finished for good. The impecunious scholar had sacrified his position for the high ideals he held regarding his responsibility. He had done it with dignity, without any fuss, and without even giving a reason for his resignation or any public explanation. But when his resignation was discussed during the Budget debate, he decided that he must speak out. In the *Nieuwe Rotterdamsche Courant* (20 December, 1898) he published a full statement of the facts, in which he did not spare De Stuers.

The counter-attack appeared in Van der Kellen's Annual Report for 1898 (he had again accepted the directorship of the Prentenkabinet), in which he made a series of accusations regarding De Groot's 'bad management' at the Print Room. When this report appeared at the end of 1899, De Groot replied at once in a pamphlet, *My directorship of the Rijks Prentenkabinet*. He analyzed the accusations one by one and showed that they were completely groundless. That he savagely attacked Van der Kellen is not surprising. Van der Kellen accused him of bad faith, and was offended that De Groot regarded Van der Kellen's nephew as unfitted for the post of assistant-director of the Print Room. But the controversy makes most unpleasant reading. De Groot lacked the gift of keeping his writings free from a polemical dogmatism, which spoiled his advocacy on this as on so many other occasions, even when there was a presumption that, as was the case here, he had right on his side.[1]

In the meantime De Groot had already found his own salvation. Now that a career in the Civil Service, in The Netherlands at least,[2] was closed to him, he had to fall back on getting his own work published. Opportunities were not difficult to find. The fame of his capability and steady application was already widespread. The catalogue of the Sammlung Schubart in Munich of 1894 was followed in 1896 by that of the Glitza collection in Hamburg. In 1897, on the advice of Fruin, the Queen Regent bestowed on him the honour of giving instruction in the Arts to the young Queen, a task which he fulfilled with the greatest devotion. In the same year he began his collaboration with Bode on the standard work on Rembrandt; this was completed in 1904. In 1898, he was appointed secretary to the great Rembrandt Exhibition, an honour that he well deserved. The following year he published a large work consisting of reproductions of Rembrandt's drawings, annotated in three languages, which showed his great knowledge and erudition. In the Historical Jubilee Book: *A Half-Century, 1848-1898,* published on the occasion of the Queen's Coronation, he wrote the chapter on 'Art and knowledge of art';

[1] Officially, the Minister could hardly do otherwise than disagree with him.
[2] At this time he was approached by Bode as to whether he would consider the directorship of the Museum in Brunswick. Although he would have liked it as a rehabilitation after the debacle in Amsterdam, there was the insurmountable difficulty that he would lose his Dutch nationality.

in a collection of essays for H. C. Rogge, he published a painting of Mijtens, in the Rennes Museum, representing 'The Marriage of the Grand Elector to Louise Henriette of Orange'; a charming gesture. In 1899, he began collaborating with Lippmann in the publication of Rembrandt's drawings; he devoted a publication to the paintings and drawings of the Utrecht churches by Pieter Saenredam and in 1900 appeared his *Verzeichniss der Gemälde in der Grossherzoglichen Gemälde-Galerie* in Mannheim. If one adds to this the series of short and long articles, mostly about the Dutch masters, particularly in *Oud Holland* and in the *Repertorium für Kunstwissenschaft,* the many book reviews in the *Nederlandsche Spectator* and in the *Nieuwe Rotterdamsche Courant* it is clear that although he left the Kabinet with empty hands, he thereafter established himself in the world of learned publications. A few years later, in 1906, on the occasion of the Rembrandt Commemoration, he was honoured with Bode, Bredius, Veth and Michel by an honorary doctorate. It was richly deserved, and the confirment caused no surprise. The commission to compile the Rembrandt Bible as part of the Rembrandt celebrations (Veth withdrew in his favour; a gesture for which De Groot was always very grateful) was an honour which he appreciated no less highly.[1] His selection as the collaborator of such scholars as Bode and Lippmann in their edition of Rembrandt's paintings and drawings in itself ensured him an international reputation; his opinions in questions of attribution were now accepted along with those of other experts. His travels not only broadened his outlook, they increased his knowledge and the number of his connections. When he undertook journeys for collectors or art dealers, they brought him financial profit as well, and this side of his work expanded rapidly. This situation, quite apart from De Groot's part in it, is an interesting phenomenon. The trade in antiques developed actively towards the end of the last century and the beginning of this one, mainly because an interest in art history had become fashionable. But at the same time, scientific criticism regarding the attribution and quality of old works of art, as practised by Bode, Bredius, De Groot and others, had given rise to doubts and uncertainties, such as could only be restored by the declaration of one of the critics that a certain work of art was indeed what it was reputed to be. Such a declaration became worth a lot of money to the trade. De Groot, who had to live mainly from this kind of thing, considered it right and proper not only to give such attestations, but also to be paid for them, in the same way as doctors and lawyers are paid for their advice.

Here I touch upon a difficult subject which in a full appreciation of De Groot's character cannot be passed over. In the last years of his life, his point of view was strongly condemned. Here lay one of the chief underlying causes of Bredius's antagonism, and it was here especially that the personal antipathy, of which I have written above, found its outlet. De Groot's certifications were often judged, particularly behind his back, somewhat unkindly, and the adverse judgments extended to his person and his personal honour.

This was completely unjustified: De Groot's integrity stands above all suspicion. He worked from a well-thought-out standpoint. But that standpoint was not shared by many other people. To arrive at an appreciation of De Groot, it is necessary to give their point of view as well.

In principle, according to this view, an expert opinion about a work of art may be considered as in the same category as a doctor's opinion or lawyer's advice, but this is only valid as long as the advice has a strict scientific significance. The position is changed as soon as the work of art with the opinion is worth more than without, in other words as soon as the certificate of

[1] His Protestant convictions played a positive role here.

opinion acquires in itself a trading value. This determines the light in which payment must be considered.

Nobody objects to the art expert being paid for attestations given, for example, in Courts of Law or in Insurance disputes, exactly like experts in other fields. The art historian can compile a scholarly catalogue of a collection for an honorarium; he can be paid when he gives a private collector regular advice about his purchases. These are all categories in which the experience gathered with much effort and knowledge can yield financial profit, without giving offence to anyone.

But to sell a scientific opinion knowing that it will be used for business profits and not for scientific or artistic ends, knowing that deplorable speculation in works of art (that is to say, in the noblest products of the human genius) will thereby be encouraged: that is entirely different, and something which goes against the conscience.

De Groot did not judge or feel in this way: in all good faith, he saw the issue in a completely intellectual light and did not allow any emotional considerations to intervene; he saw these as a confusion of pure judgement. He reasoned as follows: he gave his opinion for a fixed fee; no one was forced to come to him if he objected to the fee, and for him there was no difference whether an opinion was given ten years or a few hours before a sale.

The converse opinion mentioned above was held at that time by an increasing number of art historians and museum officials. De Groot was never able to understand this. And this is really not strange. He began by charging for advice of the kind that everyone considered permissible, and from then on the borderline cases gradually followed one after another until the stream began to get so great that he was overwhelmed and inevitably lost control of it. Doubtless there was not one moment at which the thing could recognisably be seen to have gone too far. The danger lay, moreover, not always in the payment but in the certificate itself. In giving certificates, he was not alone, no less a person than Bode also wrote them, and they had the same speculative effect.

It seems to me, there are two points of view involved here: that of the scientific spirit of the nineteenth century which shut out sentiment and social feeling, and that of the twentieth century which gives a greater place to emotional states of mind and more consideration to the interests of society. De Groot was a perfectionist of the 'entweder-oder' type: he did not understand the idea that circumstances might be able to change 'right' to 'wrong'. Thus, in spite of criticism, in spite of seeing (and complaining of) the misuse made of his attestations, he continued to give expert opinions.

The difficulties referred to here had nothing to do with the fact that among all these attestations there were some mistakes. This was also laid at his door. De Groot's method was very sound and shrewd, his knowledge and memory astonishing, the material accumulated and used for comparison and elucidation was extraordinarily comprehensive, and he went to work most conscientiously, as all who ever saw him working can testify. Nevertheless—as he himself was completely aware—there remained a possibility of error.[1] Those who thought that De Groot was slow to recognise this can be referred to the pamphlet *Knowledge of art* (1927) in which he frankly recalls several of his own mistakes (pp. 39 etc.).

[1] Among the 'mistakes', we are obliged to recall here *The laughing cavalier* of Frans Hals, which had been bought by him and declared a forgery in Court; not that we wish to stir up the unhappy story again but because De Groot felt it as a serious personal matter. He was firmly convinced that the painting was genuine. His pamphlet *Echt of Onecht? Oog of Chemie?* gives his reasons, but they were accepted by only a very few of his

But is it fair to single out the mistakes? Should one not rather in the first place establish the incontrovertible fact that, apart from the occasional error of judgement which attracts attention or is made the target of adverse comment, De Groot's intelligent and acute opinions are generally recognised as adequate and accurate? His expertise work yielded in this respect a very rich harvest; no one, not even those who regret the fact that De Groot sometimes made too much of a business of it, should lose sight of this. The over-all balance shows a very high credit figure, and for this everyone interested in Dutch Art should be profoundly grateful. But this is not his principal claim to our gratitude, there is a more important and nobler one: the fact that, in spite of the demands made on his time and energy by expertise work, he ceaselessly pursued his scholarly researches.

After his departure from Amsterdam, he established himself again in The Hague (no. 4 Heerenstraat). He was particularly occupied with his studies of Rembrandt: the great book of reproductions in collaboration with Bode and Lippmann neared completion, the third part of 'Urkunden über Rembrandt' made its appearance in the *Quellenstudiën,* and *Die Handzeichnungen Rembrandts* received the Gold Prize in the competition organised by the Teyler Society. *Johannes Vermeer and Carel Fabritius* appeared in this period, and at the same time another extensive work was begun: the revision, or more precisely a completely new edition, of Smith's work which had been published in English: *Catalogue raisonné of the works of the most eminent Dutch painters of the seventeenth century;* the new edition was published as *Beschreibendes und kritisches Verzeichniss der Werke der hervorragendsten holländischen Maler des XVII. Jahrhunderts.* This became De Groot's lifework. He worked on it until he died and he saw its completion when the tenth part was published in 1929. He employed young art historians especially to assist him in this work. Wilhelm Valentiner was the first, and perhaps because of this and because he had done most of the groundwork with De Groot, he always retained first place in De Groot's friendship and appreciation. That is not to say that the relations with the others left anything to be desired; I have always heard De Groot speak with the warmest appreciation about his collaborators. There was a series of them: Freise, Erasmus, Plietzsch, Wichmann, Lilienfeld, Elisabeth Neurdenburg, Hirschmann, Bauch, Stechow, Kauffmann, Juynboll and Gerson. On their side, they were no less grateful. On the appearance of the final instalment of the work, when De Groot invited all who could come to celebrate the occasion, they showed this appreciation in a pleasant and friendly way, by presenting him with his portrait, etched by Max Liebermann.[1]

His collaborators were mainly Germans. De Groot was definitely German-orientated in his research work. Family relations and his own student years pulled him to their side, as well as the connections with his publishers and the recognition he had found and the friendships he had made in Germany. But he was far from being one-sided in his critical appraisement. His stay in France in his youth, his membership of the French Protestant Church, were never forgotten. Among his posthumous papers is a railway map of France, on which he had characteristically traced in blue pencil the journeys he had made and marked the many places he

---

colleagues. They saw that the facile Hals imitations by modern painters had taken him by surprise; his critical method was not adapted to this situation.

It was an unfortunate affair because its notoriety damaged his prestige considerably and he suffered greatly because of it. If he had shown himself less convinced, had asserted the genuineness of the picture less often and less militantly, his friends would have been better pleased, but—the parallel case of Bode's defence of the Flora bust is another example—the fate of great experts is that they and the world pay more attention to the one cardinal mistake than to all the sound opinions which stand to their credit!

[1] A reproduction of this portrait has been included at page 18 of the present catalogue (J.B.).

had visited. No main line has been left out, and few of the secondary ones. He must have travelled repeatedly from one end of the country to the other. He was a member and faithful attender of the Walloon Church in The Hague, where he was an elder for many years.

A map of England gives the same impression. De Groot went often and gladly to England. He was an honorary member of the Burlington Fine Arts Club and had close relations with the museum world and with the antique trade. Few have studied so many private collections as De Groot did, going even to the most isolated castles. He also visited North America, where he had many connections.[1] During the first years of his period as assistant director of the Mauritshuis he went to Russia, with Bredius he travelled to Spain. He knew the museums in Italy, Austria, Hungary: everywhere where Dutch art was to be found. Switzerland was dear to him, because there he could be a tourist and take an undisturbed holiday. It was in Interlaken that he felt most at home, and in 1930 he was hoping to celebrate his twenty-fifth holiday there!

Thus the experience of this man, who had travelled all over the world and who had friends everywhere, was such as to provide a counterbalance to his German orientation. But not only that: while the thorough and systematic approach of the German temperament appealed to him, the philosophical strain which characterises German scholarship, and in this case art history, left him quite indifferent. He shrugged his shoulders at philosophy and aesthetics; he considered nothing more was needed in scholarship than the attitude of the hardheaded Dutchman. He was its most sober example, the man from Groningen.

Could it have been otherwise? He knew what he wanted to be and he accepted the consequences: Dutch nationality was for him no mere word, no empty title. This was especially striking in the last part of his life, when his work of scholarship went on calmly developing and when outside events had apparently little effect on him. For a fuller appreciation of his personality, it seems necessary to consider this in more detail.

Significant in this connection is a short note found among his posthumous papers, in which he wrote: 'The greatest disappointment of my life has been that, when for more than twenty years the personal reasons for the suspicious attitude of the government bureaus had ceased to exist,[2] no opportunity was ever found to make use of my services for the benefit of our art treasures. Once I did offer my services, on condition that it should be plainly stated during preliminary discussions that the Government approved of my ideas, which one imagines were already well-enough known, but they still replied that my services would only be considered if the offer was made without any reservations. It goes without saying that I did not make the offer a second time, even less was I inclined to make myself available for a professorial appointment.[3] As a result, my regular research has been mainly carried out within the four walls of my study, where indeed I prefer to be and have found full satisfaction. It is nevertheless a striking fact that it is this part of my work which has attracted the greatest attention in other countries.'

The 'greatest disappointment'! because he attached great importance to a position in the

[1] He went at the request of the millionaire Widener to give an opinion on his collection (his first); he condemned the greater part of it. Widener then sold this collection completely and, with the good advice, began assembling a new one.

[2] This refers probably to the resignation of V. de Stuers in 1901 as Head of the Department of Arts and Sciences; the note must have been written before February 1926 (according to a fact noted later).

[3] When in 1907 Hofstede de Groot was offered an extraordinary professorship in Art History in Leiden, he declared that he would only consider a full professorship, not only for his own prestige, but also because he considered only the latter appropriate in Rembrandt's native city.

Civil Service? Certainly not; he knew only too well that his freedom gave him more opportunity to work, and work was his pleasure.

The cause lay deeper: he had the feeling that as a civil servant he could serve his country with all his strength, and that service was necessary to him, a necessity born out of gratitude and sense of duty. In all his international relations and the wide horizons which he reached through his work, De Groot always regarded it a privilege to be a Dutchman, a privilege for which he must make a personal sacrifice. Now that this state service was closed to him, after he had turned his back on it, he considered that he could still partially fulfil his duty: when people called for his collaboration in affairs connected directly or indirectly with his research work, he would give that help to the full. Given the thoroughly systematic quality which marked De Groot's work, he did not do this because he found it agreeable, or because the matter interested him particularly, or because it provided pleasant variety. No, he did it simply from a deep-rooted and highly cherished sense of duty. Nevertheless, his performance of it was no less thorough, no less devoted than his attention to the work which was dearest to him and accorded completely with his nature. Those who have worked with him at administrative meetings and on committees can witness to this: no effort was too much for him, in studying papers or whatever other task was necessary.

As early as 1905 he became the vice-chairman of The Hague Historical Society and in 1909 its Chairman, and when in 1927 he resigned he had served in all eighteen years as member of the Committee and had been Chairman eleven times. In 1913 he was one of the founders of the Society whose aim was to save Huygens' 'Hofwyck' in Voorburg from oblivion; this was restored under his chairmanship and opened to the public. In 1912, by a strange twist of fate, he followed De Stuers as member of the Management Committee of The Hague Museum. I was appointed Director practically at the same time and as he continued to serve until his death, I know better than anyone else how seriously he took this position and whenever it was necessary how much he gave to it. For me this was undoubtedly of great importance, for his experience and knowledge stood me in good stead. But more than once, it brought me great problems, particularly during the time when we were planning the new museum, when our ideas clashed. Then he was inflexible. But he knew how to distinguish between business differences and personal friendship and appreciation, so that even the sharpest differences of opinion did not spoil our friendship. I had to admire the devotion and the seriousness with which he took his responsibility, and I must not forget to record an instance of how readily and quickly he could acknowledge that he was mistaken: my design for lighting techniques, to which he strongly objected, was tested out and proved to have the advantages I had claimed and which he had held to be imaginary. He was always responsive to facts; he was rarely convinced by reasoning. De Groot was therefore a formidable opponent, here as elsewhere. But on the other hand, wherever he went he contributed an enormous amount of constructive work, sound information and disinterested help. He was also, as is seldom the case with mediocre opponents, most loyal in his collaboration in executing a decision, even one taken against his advice, as long as that decision was taken in a formally correct manner (the qualification is typical for De Groot). Such opposition forces one to consider very carefully one's own standpoint, to crystallise one's opinion and to guard against hasty decisions. In this way, De Groot could be of the greatest help, even when in opposition.

Apart from The Hague Museum, the Frans Hals Museum in Haarlem benefited from his collaboration. There also, as in my own case, the director received special support in that De Groot was always on guard to see that the Committee's methods were not those of the 'De

Stuers régime' and that the director's responsibilities were not infringed. It was mainly due to his support that The Hague Management Committee quickly became unofficially, and afterwards officially, an Advisory Committee.

De Groot's high regard for the responsibility of the museum director did not prevent him from considering for a short time, the possibility of an appointment as Inspector-General of Museums, an officer whose authority and influence was to bring order and uniformity into the field of museum administration, a field in which there were a good many rather untidy growths. The idea was, if I remember aright, originally put forward by Mr. Muller and discussed in a pamphlet (on which De Groot had worked), published by the *Nederlandsche Oudheidkundige Bond*.[1] Later when it was again brought before the meeting of the State Commission, there was very little enthusiasm for it on the part of the Government or the museum world, and nothing came of it. De Groot did not relish the idea of being merely a member of the newly formed State Advisory Commission on museums.

But I have here anticipated the most important episode in De Groot's public life during these years: his secretaryship of the State Commission for Museum Affairs, set up in 1919. Here again, De Groot had played an important part in its previous history. In 1911, the *Oudheid-kundige Bond* had decided that at their winter meeting they would bring forward subjects of importance to museums. De Groot opened the series, reporting on museum budgets. In the following summer, when Moes had spoken about provincial museums, a committee was set up to formulate proposals regarding the direction and planning of such museums. The activities of this committee, to which S. Muller and De Groot belonged, became more and more extensive until it was eventually asked to assemble all the proposals, which had been accepted from time to time, into one explanatory pamphlet.

In addition to the two gentlemen mentioned above, Messrs. Pit, Veth, Vogelsang and the author were members of the committee. The work of the drafting committee had to wait several years before any progress was made. It was a long-drawn-out affair. Originally Muller had the guiding hand; he divided the work at his discretion and, for example, asked Veth to handle one particular subject and Vogelsang another. De Groot thought that both subjects fell within his own competence and ought to have been allotted to him. Confusion! Muller plied his fellow members with detailed notes, to which De Groot attached no less detailed marginal memoranda. At a certain moment, Muller, De Groot and Veth had all sent in their resignations to the secretary of the committee. It took an enormous amount of trouble to soothe all the hurt feelings. In this affair, De Groot was the most generous, but the other two did not understand his rather formal attitude. In the end, De Groot replaced Muller as Chairman and all the articles were completed. Everyone was prepared to sign in peace and amity. Quite early on, I had gauged the contrast between De Groot and Veth. This was not only a difference in sensitiveness and an obvious difference in temperament, more or less the same things that estranged Bredius and De Groot. There was also in this case a difference in practical approach, which had not yet really come to the surface, but was to appear in the following phase of their collaboration. There was in addition the factor that however much he admired Veth's artistry as a portrait painter, De Groot did not regard Veth as a fully competent art historian, while for Bredius he always felt great admiration,[2] as well as lifelong gratitude for

[1] *Over Hervorming en beheer onzer musea,* appeared in 1918.

[2] He esteemed Bredius' own opinion highly: he considered that Bredius allowed himself to be too much influenced by the younger men, for whose opinion De Groot had no such admiration.

all that he owed him. This regard was shown when, in 1915, he headed a committee which honoured Bredius on the occasion of his sixtieth birthday with a collection of Bredius' essays.[1] De Groot used to delight in telling how he had caught Veth out on various occasions and made him look ridiculous; for example, when he got him to accept a reproduction as a genuine Rembrandt drawing, or to assert that a heavily restored painting was one in its original state. These were trivial reprisals against Veth, who had in his turn played practical jokes on De Groot, which had not always been easy to laugh off!

Before long came a sharp conflict of deeper significance. An independent Department of Education, Art and Science was established with the energetic Dr. de Visser as its first director, and with Mr. M. Duparc, a man of intelligence and drive, as the new chief of the department. All this opened up new possibilities for the museum world. Everyone at the Department also realized that first of all the existing situation must be exhaustively studied and radically changed. The *Oudheidkundige Bond*'s pamphlet showed the way. This led to the setting up of the above mentioned State Commission, in which the members of the *Bondscommissie* were included (with the exception of Pit who, alas! refused). As the number of members was increased to twenty-two, Bredius, Six and Schmidt-Degener, among others, could be brought in. Duparc was fortunate in that De Groot undertook the secretaryship: it was De Groot who had the most systematic grasp on the subject, and who, in particular, would not rest before a decision had been taken and formulated, even when concerned with the smallest problem.[2]

Matters developed otherwise than De Groot had expected or wished. He had imagined an expansion and implementation of the recommendations made by the *Bond*; the adoption of more systematization, a better definition of authority, close inspection and far-reaching rules of procedure, as well as augmentation of museum budgets through increased income, formation of funds etc. The conclusions reached regarding all these important things are in great measure due to De Groot's work. But to De Groot's annoyance, I believe, these points were of minor importance to the Commission when seen in the framework of its work as a whole.

Moreover, between the formulation of the *Bond*'s proposals during the years 1911–14 and the meeting of the State Commission lay the World War, with its enormous influence on cultural life, its 'Umwertung aller Werte'. So that now, under totally different circumstances, a museum commission had to consider not only the function of the museum as an institute of culture, but the very meaning of art, of Beauty and all the accompanying emotions and their place in the new world.

De Groot was not the right man for this situation, for he lacked the necessary sensibility and imagination. I have referred to this facet of his character already.

Veth approached the problem from exactly the opposite standpoint; with his keen and lively mind he was conscious, as an artist, of the paramount importance of such questions. When Veth, with a certain degree of triumph over De Groot, could put up an argument against the pamphlet of De Groot's pupil Valentiner: *Umgestaltung der Museen im Sinne der neuen Zeit,*[3] De Groot was very amazed; seen in retrospect the argumentation was rather exaggerated. De Groot defended himself valiantly and skilfully, but because the psychology and philosophy underlying the ideas of his opponents escaped him, his argument was rarely

[1] He himself made up the greatest part of the rather large deficit on the costs of the edition.

[2] On the dissolution of the Commission, the Government showed their appreciation by recommending him as Knight of the Order of the Nederlandsche Leeuw.

[3] Grote'sche Verlagsbuchhandlung, Berlin, 1919.

effective, and neither his powers of reasoning nor his personal charm availed him. Although they shared his views on many points, neither Six nor Muller remained unaffected by the new ideas. And so, in spite of all his knowledge, his sincere devotion, the enormous amount of work which he had contributed and the time that he had sacrificed, De Groot was left with the feeling that his work had been in vain.

Perhaps I put the conflict too strongly, more sharply at least than the parties concerned saw it themselves at the time, but even so I believe that De Groot must have felt it deeply when he declined to accept further responsibility for the conduct of museum affairs as member of the Museum Council, 'where Veth would rule the roost'.[1]

The outcome of this conflict can be seen as tragic because it can be regarded as the realization that the study of Art History in De Groot's sense, that is, a discipline in which 'connoisseurship' was the prime objective, was unacceptable, not for himself, but to the future leaders of museum affairs and the younger generation. All that we have hitherto been saying of this new and widely accepted orientation of knowledge was thus brought home to De Groot. He must have been deeply grieved to feel that he had no pupils to follow in his footsteps, that he had been unable to found a school, and had received no appreciation from the younger generation. But he would not have been De Groot, tough, energetic and persevering, if he had allowed himself to be disconcerted or to deviate from his chosen path—if indeed such an idea had ever occurred to him, for he had full confidence that his was the only right way, and that after fruitless wanderings, the others would in due time recognize it as such.

He was not yet ready for 'Umgestaltung im Sinne der neuen Zeit'; he did not feel any need for it: the 'preservation' of the firmly established forms of Beauty satisfied him. But let us acknowledge that a thing is not better just because it is new, and a conservatism like De Groot's, which was born not out of aversion to new things but out of a sincere love of the old, has the right to be judged as a virtue.

There was yet another more or less official function that made calls on De Groot's time for many years: his membership of the *Rijks Monumenten Commissie*. Some time before, in an essay in the *Bulletin* of the *Nederlandsche Oudheidkundige Bond* in 1912, and again in his appreciative review of Kalf's book on the Baronie of Breda, De Groot made the complaint that the art of painting had not been given enough attention in the inventories of the *Rijks Commissie*. A few months later, by Royal Decree of 18 July, 1916, he was appointed member of the former Inventory Commission, and as early as 1917[2] the 'provisional list of Gelderland' showed signs of his collaboration. This collaboration was thorough. He covered systematically, in succession, various parts of the country, and from his findings produced the detailed definitive inventory of everything pertaining to his special field. Thus the basis was laid for the future work of the commission, at least as far as the paintings were concerned. The outsider saw only a little of the result of all this work, an example of the truly devoted 'worker bee's' industry which characterized De Groot. But even so one can get an idea of what this work involved if one looks at the series of 'provisional lists' made with his collaboration. I have mentioned Gelderland (1917). This was followed by North Holland (1921), Zeeland (1922), Overijssel (1923), Limburg (1926), Amsterdam (1928) and North Holland II (1930). The tempo at which these useful, introductory essays appeared is a measure of the inner urge which spurred

[1] Posthumous notes.

[2] On the reorganization in 1918 of the *Rijks Monumenten Commissie*, he became member of Department A.

De Groot on. In these 'provisional lists' he not only wrote the notes on paintings but also treated several districts and cities in all their aspects.

This was the kind of work which suited De Groot. It followed in the direct line of the many Baedeker notes which he had produced, and which had put innumerable people in his debt— anonymously! He made these Baedeker notes gladly; he found travelling a pleasure in itself and he understood its art. There was no one who provided so much unusual information, even about the most out-of-the-way places and journeys. It was certainly not purely out of interest in art history that he followed the travelling artist, Lambert Doomer, with such persistence, and traced and collected his topographical drawings, or completed his collection of Roghman's castle series. One of the most interesting of these experiments was surely his successful effort to reconstruct the Swiss journey of Hercules Seghers (*Oud Holland*, 1927), whereby he was able to locate several of this wonderful master's paintings. It was a painting in his own collection, undubitably one of its crowning features, whith started him on this track.

With this phase we come to the part of De Groot's life that forms, as it were, a climax because here is shown most clearly, and for always, the lasting significance of his devotion to his fatherland.

As soon as his work brought him in an income that covered more than the barest necessities of his day-to-day existence, De Groot began to collect and buy whatever he found beautiful and interesting. This is the proof of his true love for art in itself, even though he would not admit that it was on the plane of 'intoxication with beauty'.[1] This collection grew quickly and contained important works, thanks to his expert knowledge and the many opportunities that came his way: paintings, drawings, and, later on, pottery and silver and Italian medals. The painting of Hercules Seghers, Fabritius' *Warrior*, the Ludolf de Jong, the series of Rembrandt drawings, the series of drawings of nearly all the old Dutch masters, the Pisanello and the Pasti medals: all these were part of his collection, one of the best private collections in Holland. It was his pride and joy and continual source of daily pleasure. He was especially happy when, in his house on the Voorhout, no. 94, he was able to give his collection a worthy setting. He could not bear to part with it during his lifetime, he could not forego the pleasure which it gave him just to look at it. But even so, he donated the best pieces he possessed, retaining the use of them during his life. Most noteworthy is undoubtedly the series of no less than sixty-five Rembrandt drawings, among which were some of the most beautiful and most important, acquired by the Rijks Prentenkabinet. On the occasion of the opening of the new university buildings in Groningen, where both his grandfathers had been professors, the city was given the choice of his important collection of drawings and, moreover, the cream of his collection of paintings.[2]

At one move, the Groningen Museum was lifted impressively above its former status. It gave him great satisfaction that Groningen was so grateful and showed its thanks. He implemented his gift on two other occasions. He left his costly Italian medals to The Hague Museum. He began collecting these because Rembrandt used a motif of the Gonzaga medal for his etching *The three crosses*, and once having come under the fascination of the wonderful modelling in costly bronze, he continued to collect. He attached a condition to the gift, namely that, with the agreement of the Government, the Rijkspenningkabinet should be

[1] Posthumous notes.

[2] The Rijksmuseum was allowed to exchange the Hercules Seghers and Groningen received a large Willem van de Velde in its place.

34

housed in the new Municipal Museum. This condition was typical of De Groot. An old wish of his played a great role here, combining an expansion of the collection by more efficient exploitation and the emergence of the Penningkabinet from its unfortunate isolation. It was a survival of the 'system' which had been drawn up for the museums in The Hague by De Groot (with others) in 1918.[1] It was the only part that remained, since the idea of removing the collection from the Mauritshuis to another building was rejected by the Government; had this idea been accepted, the Groningen collection would also have been left to the Mauritshuis. I believe that De Groot himself later realised that, although no one would deny its deficiencies, the Mauritshuis had a tradition which should on no account be broken. He did not refer to the matter again in the State Commission. To go back to his collection, we see that several small gifts were made to the museums in Haarlem and Leiden, representative of the masters who had worked in those cities.

Finally, I come to one of his most important steps, his arrangements for the disposal of his study material. These reproductions and notes were given to the Government on the condition that they should be expanded and made available to anyone who wished to consult them; this accorded with his strongly held principles.

It sounds so simple! 'Study material' when used by such a man has a very wide connotation! It includes the series of books so carefully assembled, bound in dark red, which grew continually over the years, containing photographs and other reproductions of all the examples of old Dutch painting, of which De Groot was the great connoisseur; a rare study collection and indispensable comparative material for the expert and scholar. There were ordinary photographs which anyone could buy, certainly, but also a great many found in and acquired from obscure corners of the world and assembled with great trouble, involving lengthy correspondence—all were photographs with a history, and this collection was of great help to more than one student struggling in his research work. In addition to the cupboard containing the reproductions, there was a series of long green boxes with card indexes, recording the details of artists, their work, their lives; also notes relating to paintings and their history and provenance, extracted from innumerable sale-room catalogues and other sources. During his lifetime, with unusual generosity, De Groot gave everyone permission to search here. There can be no art historian, working in the last twenty years on any aspect of the history of Dutch art of the seventeenth century, who does not owe a debt of gratitude not only for the opportunity to use that material, but also to the man who brought it together.

That all this has not been lost but preserved for the nation, and under good guidance will remain to be put to good use, is certainly not least of De Groot's titles to the gratitude of our country, which he loved and served in his own wise manner.

The solid achievement which he left behind crowns his life, a life of deep devotion to his Fatherland.

In the midst of his work De Groot is gone. On 7 April 1930, he suddenly collapsed. The apparent seriousness of his illness soon gave rise to fears that this must mean the end of his work, but it was not realized that it was so near. As early as 14 April, it was all over. His eldest sister, always so close to him, was with him. He died surrounded by his art collection, in the front room which his many friends and visitors knew so well. His funeral at Oud-Eikenduin was simple and impressive and attended by a large gathering. Naturally, there were the many

[1] Report for the Association for Trade, Industry and Municipal Interests.

people who had had contact with De Groot through their work, scholars and government officials. There was also the smaller circle of those who knew him personally, members of The Hague Historical Society, which he had helped to found; he had punctually attended the monthly meetings and was a welcome guest, whose words carried authority, he had been a gracious host whose well-prepared lectures were eagerly listened to. And then there were the more intimate friends, the table-companions of the 'De Witte' Club, in whose company he could be at his ease, with whom he played chess and billiards, with whom he sometimes went on holidays and who knew him as a jolly, witty, companionable man, even if in the somewhat stiff Dutch manner which went with his character. And finally his family, to whom he meant even more, faithful and devoted, full of consideration and meticulous in his attentions; from them he did not have to hide his tenderness. This side of his character he kept instinctively hidden, while to the world he showed the stiff, diffident and even unapproachable figure, which people label as 'his type'.

Was he his own enemy? It seems to me not improbable. I see him before me, then, finally as an almost tragic figure in certain respects: a man most gifted in mind and intellect, filled with a strong sense of duty, wholly absorbed in his work, who had achieved so much,[1] producing useful, original, fruitful work, but who still in the isolation of his study must have had the feeling that life had withheld much from him, and that much of the blame lay with his own personality, that extraordinarily complex personality to which his talents and the circumstances of his life had given form and expression.

H. Meijer, commissioned by friends and admirers, painted De Groot's portrait to celebrate his sixtieth birthday. The crowded canvas (the style and composition were approved by the sitter) truly reveals that tragic loneliness.

H. E. VAN GELDER[2]

[1] With all that had been achieved and completed, one piece of work remained unfinished, namely *The history and development of the art collection of our Royal House,* although he had begun to work on it early (see *Verslag Mauritshuis* 1894) with his very understandable love for the subject. A single article on it was published (see no. 311) and his last work for *Oud Holland* (see no. 422) was closely connected with it. But the compilation of the inventories was practically complete, and Dr. Schneider undertook to finish the work with De Groot's collaborator, E. van Biema. The study of 'the funeral processions of the Nassaus' was also left unfinished.

[2] I am deeply indebted to those who have assisted me by giving information and helping in other ways in the writing of this obituary; above all, to Mrs. Posthumus Meyes, *née* Hofstede de Groot, who put her brother's enormous collection of letters and notes at my disposal.

CATALOGUE

1. Hendrik Averkamp, *Skating scene*

1. Hendrik Averkamp, *Skating scene* p. 38

DATA: Pen and bistre, aquarelle, white body-colour, on white paper, 141 x 195 mm. Recto, lower left corner: signed 'HA'. Verso: owner's mark Von Heyl zu Herrnsheim (Lugt 2897) and 'no. 131'.

LITERATURE: Henkel 1916, p. 339; Hirschmann, p. 404; Becker, no. 1*; Welcker, no. T36, no. T38 and no. T626; Van Puyvelde, p. 10.

EXHIBITIONS: Leiden 1903, no. 71; Leiden 1916A, no. 8; The Hague 1930, I no. 22; Groningen 1931, no. 29; Groningen 1948, no. 85; Groningen 1952, no. 2; The Hague 1955, no. 5; Ingelheim 1964, no 3*.

PROVENANCE: Sale Goll van Franckenstein, Amsterdam 1.7.1833, Kbk E no. 11 (L. 13362;) Sale Von Heyl zu Herrnsheim, Stuttgart 25.5.1903, no. 34; — Collection Hofstede de Groot, inv. no. 300, bequest 1914, no. 3; — Groninger Museum voor Stad en Lande, inv. no. 1931–128.

In her catalogue of drawings by Hendrik Averkamp, Dr Welcker is evidently mistaken in listing four drawings by Averkamp in the Hofstede de Groot Bequest to Groningen. The numbers T36 and T38 represent in fact one and the same drawing, whereas each of the two drawings mentioned under no. T37 should have had a separate number. The descriptions of nos. T36 and T38 both apply to our drawing, while measurements (erroneously given as 111 x 195 mm), provenance and literature point to the same conclusion. In addition to this, no. T626 is also identical with the present drawing. Welcker's suggestion that our drawing (T36) might be a copy, to be compared with no. T6[1] requires further consideration in view of this misunderstanding. As Dr Welcker accepts (T38) and at the same time rejects (T36) our drawing we may conclude that she probably relied on others in her judgement on authenticity. The reason for this confusion is understandable. There exist at least three, and probably four drawings representing a skating scene which show to the left a small piece of land on which two onlookers are standing. Two of these are the drawings already mentioned at Groningen and Hamburg. The third is in Amsterdam.[2] A fourth drawing of this kind appeared at a sale in Amsterdam,[3] a winter scene with a lady and gentleman in the left foreground; upon the ice, horse-drawn sleighs with a lady and gentlemen, and several figures disporting themselves. According to the measurements[4] given in the catalogue of this sale, this drawing could not be one of the first three. A number of similar details may be noticed. The man binding on his skate in the drawings in Groningen and in Amsterdam is the same, as is also the man cutting the ice with his axe. The group of the horse-drawn sleigh with two men and a woman appears in the drawings at Hamburg and Groningen. The spectators in the left foreground at Amsterdam and Hamburg are the same also. For all four drawings the same composition has been used: in the left foreground a man and a woman are standing, looking at a large number of people disporting themselves upon the ice, while on the right a windmill and a boat, frozen in the ice, can be seen.

We may safely assume that drawings like these four were meant as small paintings, made for their own sake, intended to be sold to the public, in contrast to quickly-drawn studies after nature. This view, already expressed by Welcker,[5] is strengthened by inscriptions on the drawings in Hamburg[6] and in the collection of F. Lugt.[7]

Instead of regarding one of these drawings as a copy of the others, it would be better to assume that they were all made within a certain period in which Averkamp used the above-mentioned composition-principle, and made frequent use of a number of sketches, drawn earlier after nature. Also the quality of our drawing does not suggest a copy.

Fortunately the drawing in Hamburg bears in verso, along with the inscription, the date 1630. Another drawing in Amsterdam,[8] which by virtue of several similarities in composition and details belongs to our group, can be dated 1625, according to an engraving by S. Fokke.[9] We may safely place our drawing in the last decade of Averkamp's activity on the strength of these two dates. Mr. Haga, of the Rijksmuseum, Amsterdam, informs us that there is a copy of our drawing[10] which must have been made around the year 1820, according to a topographical particularity of a drawing in verso.

Fig. 1. Hendrik Averkamp, *Skating scene*. Drawing, Hamburg, Kunsthalle

[1] Hamburg, Kunsthalle, inv. no. 34085 (Fig. 1). An eighteenth-century copy at Rijksmuseum Kröller-Müller, Otterloo, inv. no. 9K.   [2] Welcker no. T23, Museum Fodor, Amsterdam, inv. no. 5. Exhibited Ingelheim 1964, no. 4*.   [3] Sale C. Smitt, Amsterdam 4.12.1780, no. 457.   [4] 11½ x 12½ duim (about the same as inches).   [5] p. 85.   [6] 'Dit heeft de Stom tot Campen gedaen cost 6 gr ad 1630 dat. is veel meer waer ... is genaem Handrik van Avercam zyn const is in goed estym.' For this text we are indebted to Dr. Wolf Stubbe, Hauptkustos der Hamburger Kunsthalle.   [?] Inv. no. 4953: 'Hendrik Averkamp heeft mij dit geleverd [?] 28 Januarij 1613 in Campen.' We are indebted to Mr. Carlos van Hasselt, Keeper of the collections of the Institut Néerlandais in Paris, for kindly giving us this information.   [8] Rijksprentenkabinet, inv. no. A240, Welcker no. TII.   [9] Hollstein I, p. 45, no. 4.   [10] Coll. Mr. A.S.J. Baron van der Feltz, Brummen.

2. Hendrik Averkamp, *Pastry-cook in front of a tent* p. 42

DATA: Pen and bistre, aquarelle, on white paper, 123 x 162 mm. Verso: studies of figures and a sleigh.* Watermark no. 1.

LITERATURE: Hirschmann, p. 404; Van Regteren Altena 1931, p. 73*; Welcker, no. T37.

EXHIBITIONS: Leiden 1916A, no. 9; The Hague 1930, I no. 23; Groningen 1931, no. 27; Groningen 1952, no. 3*; The Hague 1955, no 7.

PROVENANCE: Sale C. van den Berg, Haarlem 29.8.1775, no. 80 (L. 2439); Anonymous sale, Paris 6.5.1909, no. 1; — Collection Hofstede de Groot, inv. no. 361, bequest 1914, no. 1; — Groninger Museum voor Stad en Lande, inv. no. 1931–126.

This drawing from Averkamp's later years is, in contrast with the preceding one, a study after nature, not meant to be sold by the artist as a little painting. E. Trautscholdt, in his article 'De oude koekebakster, Nachtrag zu Adriaan Brouwer',[1] does not mention our drawing. There is an important difference here from other versions of the theme. In our drawing the pastry-cook is sitting out of doors, in a tent, whereas in the three engravings that Averkamp could have known[2] the scene is indoors. Consequently, we do not think that our drawing has a direct connection with the versions of the theme mentioned by Trautscholdt. On the other

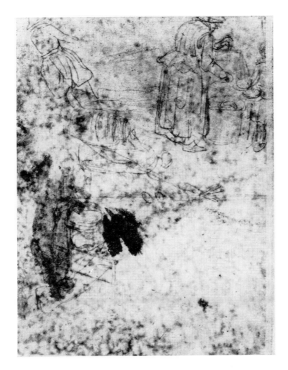

Fig. 2. Hendrik Averkamp, *Studies of figures and a sleigh*. Drawing, verso of cat. no. 2

hand we may assume that Averkamp, when seeing the scene during his wanderings, remembered that it was a pictorial subject, as he would probably have been in touch with current events like any other painter of his time. No impressions of the engraving by H. Spilman after this drawing, recorded by Welcker, are known, according to Hollstein I, p. 45.

[1] In *Pantheon* XIX, 1961, Heft 4, p. 187.   [2] (1) P. van der Heyden, 1567; Wurzbach I, p. 150, no. 18. (2) Jan van de Velde; Franken and Van der Kellen, no. 109. (3) Jan Matham; Wurzbach I, p. 199, no. 18.

3. Hendrik Averkamp, *Two fishermen in a boat* p. 43

DATA: Pen and bistre, aquarelle, on white paper 85 x 255 mm. Verso: two fragments of lead-pencil sketches: head of a man with a bonnet, and a door of a hut.
LITERATURE: Henkel 1916, p. 339; Hirschmann, p. 404; Welcker, no. T37 and T550.
EXHIBITIONS: Leiden 1916A, no.10; The Hague 1930, I no. 21; Groningen 1931, no. 28; Groningen 1948, no. 84; Groningen 1952, no. 4; The Hague 1955, no. 6; Vancouver 1958, no. 2.

2. Hendrik Averkamp, *Pastry-cook in front of a tent*

3. Hendrik Averkamp, *Two fishermen in a boat*

PROVENANCE: Sale J. Roelofs, Amsterdam 8.3.1824, Kbk p. no. 8 (L. 10608); Sale H. Duval a.o., Amsterdam 22.6.1910, no. 288; — Collection Hofstede de Groot, inv. no. 362, bequest 1914, no. 2; — Groninger Museum voor Stad en Lande, inv. no. 1931–127.

Like the preceding number, the present drawing probably is a study after nature. We do not find the scene in other drawings or paintings by Averkamp. One drawing,[1] showing two men and a woman in a boat, can hardly be regarded as having a direct connection. The catalogue of the exhibition at Leiden in the year 1916 gives erroneously: *'three* fishermen in a boat.' At the Duval sale the drawing was catalogued as Jan Porcellis.

[1] Sale Huldschinsky, Berlin 3.11.1931, no. 6, Welcker no. T550.

4 and 5. David Bailly, *Portraits of Reyer Pouwelsz. van Reygersberch and his wife, Aeltgen Cornelisdr. van Onderwater*   p. 136, 137

DATA: Brush-drawing and black ink, grey wash on vellum 155 x 129 mm. Recto, lower left corner: 'D. bailly. fecit.', lower right corner: 'A°. 1628.'. Pasted on paper.
LITERATURE: Moes, p. 146; Henkel 1916, p. 342; Hirschmann, p. 406*; Henkel 1931, Pl. XXVIb; Bruyn, p. 154, note no. 5 and p. 121 ff.
EXHIBITIONS: Leiden 1916A, nos. 11 and 12; The Hague 1930, I nos. 24 and 25; Groningen 1931, nos. 30 and 31; Groningen 1952, nos. 5 and 6; The Hague 1955, nos. 8 and 9.
PROVENANCE: Sale The Hague, 8.3.1869, no. 3 (L. 31051); — Sale The Hague 28.5.1872, no. 5 (L. 33247); — Sale Van der Willigen, The Hague 12.8.1874, no. 6 (L. 35065); — Collection B. Suermondt; — Sale F. A. v. S., Amsterdam 11.6.1912, no. 312*; — Collection Hofstede de Groot, inv. nos. 383 and 384, bequest 1914, nos. 4 and 5; — Groninger Museum voor Stad en Lande, inv. nos. 1931–129 and 1931–130.

Two good examples of Bailly's rather stereotyped portraits, of which quite a number are preserved. His technique, inspired by engravings, seldom varies, the pose and costumes of his sitters being often alike. From the articles by Prof. Bruyn on David Bailly[1] we learn that the artist had a predilection for still-life. Here also the portraits are conceived as a small still-life, with a hint of *trompe l'œuil* and a picture-in-a-picture in it. The two drawings were regarded as portraits of Nicolaas van Reigersbergen and his wife, but Bruyn did not agree with this identification, a.o. on the grounds that Nicolaas van Reigersbergen, Counsellor of the High Court of Justice of Holland, was not married. Bailly perhaps painted a portrait[2] of Reigersbergen's sister Maria, who was married to Hugo de Groot, but this identification is also disputable when compared with documented portraits.[3]

The possibility of these drawings being portraits of the artist and his wife must also be considered, as there is a resemblance with a documented self-portrait of Bailly.[4] Against this identification, however, stands the fact that Bailly married as late as 1643, whereas the portraits are dated 1628. Furthermore this resemblance seems to extend to almost all the male portraits by Bailly, a particularity probably due to the limited repertoire and technique of the artist.

Already at the anonymous sale in The Hague[5] the two portraits were described as 'Portraits de Nicolaas Reigersbergen, beau-frère de H. Grotius, et de son épouse, 2 pièces. A la plume, lavé d'encre de Chine.' It is possible that the portraits were connected traditionally with the name Reigersbergen, and that the nineteenth century, with its penchant for historical colour-ing, is responsible for the addition of the Christian name Nicolas.

Mr. E. Pelinck, of Leiden, has made the helpful suggestion that we should not too readily reject the traditional identification, drawing our attention to a family called Reygersberch, a Leiden family which is only indirectly related to the Counsellor of the High Court of Justice.[6]

A further warning not to abandon the name Reygersberch too easily was the coincidence that in the inventory of 'vrouwe Sara Johanna Bailly, weduwe van de Heer Hendrik Hop, voormalig Bewinthebber van de Oost Indische Compagnie', drawn up at Amsterdam, 24th february 1724,[7] there is the following entry: '2 bloemenkransjes, geschildert door Juffr. Reygersbergen,' although the exact family relationship could not be established.[8] In the municipal archives at Leiden[9] a certain Reyer Pouwelsz. van Reygersberch is mentioned, who was married to Aeltgen Cornelisdr. van Onderwater.[10] Reyer Pouwelsz. van Reygersberch was a carpenter, and unfor-tunately nothing definite is known about his birth and origin. The possibility exists, however, that he was the grandson of Meester Jacob van Reygersberch, of the Leiden family Gorter van Reygersberch. This Meester Jacob is said to have been unmarried, and is supposed to have been the last male scion of this family; Mr. Pelinck, though, found evidence of this Jacob having had children.

Aeltgen van Onderwater was the daughter of a carpenter whose only son died at sea in 1629. We may assume that Reyer took over the business of his father-in-law. Aeltgen was born ca. 1602. They had a daughter Aechgen, who was mentioned as being an orphan in 1638. It seems plausible that their wedding-day would have been in or around the year 1628.

To recapitulate the facts, we have in the first place the traditional identification with a married couple bearing the name of Reygersberg. A cousin of David Bailly possessed two flower pieces by a woman named Reygersbergen. A Reyer Pouwelsz. van Reygersberch married ca. 1628 Aeltgen Cornelisdr. van Onderwater; this is the only couple of that name in Leiden at that time who, so far as the sources permit us to conclude, could be considered as possible sitters. As the portraits are not incompatible with the social status and age of the sitters, we offer hypothetically the identification of a wedding-portrait of Reyer Pouwelsz. Reygersberch and Aeltgen Cornelisdr. van Onderwater.

[1] See Bibliography Bruyn, p. 154 and p. 160.   [2] Rijksmuseum, Amsterdam, inv. no. 407.   [3] Bruyn, p. 160.   [4] Signed and dated 1625. Amsterdam, Printroom of the Rijksmuseum, inv. no. 140–7.   [5] See provenance.   [6] Mr. Jacob Reygersberch was a second cousin of Hugo de Groot, who married Nicolaas van Reigersbergen's sister Maria.   [7] Protocol Notaris M. Schriek, Amsterdam.   [8] Both these branches of the Bailly family originate from Antwerp.   [9] The genealogical data about the families Reigersbergen, Onderwater and Bailly we owe to the kind collaboration of the staff of the Leiden municipal archives.   [10] In all probability this Aeltgen van Onderwater was not related to Claudine Jansdr. van Onderwater, whose portrait was done by Bailly in 1633, together with that of her husband Ripperd van Groenendijk.

6. Cornelis Bega, *Study of a seated woman, facing to the right*   p. 135

DATA: Sanguine on white paper 231 x 176 mm. Verso: owner's mark Von Heyl zu Herrnsheim (Lugt 2879).

LITERATURE: Hirschmann, p. 210.

EXHIBITIONS: Leiden 1903, no. 68; Leiden 1916C, no. 5; The Hague 1930, I no. 27; Groningen 1931, no. 33.

PROVENANCE: Sale Von Heyl zu Herrnsheim, Stuttgart 25.5.1903, no. 44; — Collection Hofstede de Groot, inv. no. 201, bequest 1914, no. 7; — Groninger museum voor Stad en Lande, inv. no. 1931–132.

See text of the next entry.

7. Cornelis Bega, *Study of a seated woman, facing to the left* p. 138

DATA: Sanguine on white paper 239 x 183 mm. Verso: owner's mark Von Heyl zu Herrnsheim (Lugt 2879).
LITERATURE: Hirschmann, p. 210.
EXHIBITIONS: Leiden 1903, no. 68; Leiden 1916C, no. 6; The Hague 1930, I no. 26; Groningen 1931, no. 32; Groningen 1948, no. 86; The Hague 1955, no. 10.
PROVENANCE: Sale Von Heyl zu Herrnsheim, Stuttgart 25.5.1903, no. 45; — Collection Hofstede de Groot, inv. no. 202, bequest 1914, no. 6; — Groninger Museum voor Stad en Lande, inv. no. 1931–131.

Quite a number of seventeenth century artists have adopted this kind of figure-study in sanguine, with sitting and standing women. To verify the traditional attribution to Cornelis Bega, it is essential to pick out the characteristics from documented or generally accepted works of the master. Those characteristics are found in the technique in general and in the way in which Bega draws a hand. Especially the latter fact is significant in comparison with e.g. Gerrit Berckheyde, with whose work there could be some confusion. From a signed drawing in Vienna[1] we can see how Bega conceives a hand as a silhouette, first outlining the mass of the hand and only afterwards making a subdivision in stereotype, impersonal and rather thick fingers. In a drawing in London[2] the hands are also merely given in silhouette, not even subdivided. The same kind of hands as in our drawing can be seen in a study in Paris,[3] in which the woman's right hand is even exactly the same as the right hand of the woman in our drawing no. 7. Sometimes other painters may have used the same method of drawing hands. Incidentally Berkheyde did this,[4] but no other artist used it so frequently as Bega in combination with the striking thickness of the hands that we see in our drawings. This and the similarity to a group of drawings, generally accepted as Bega, in the collection of the late Victor de Stuers[5] inclines us not to alter the attribution.

[1] Sitting woman, Albertina; reproduced in Albertina Publications, ed. Schenk, no. 744. [2] Sitting woman, collection Sir Robert Witt; exh. Brussels 1937–38, no. 121, Pl. LXXV. [3] Standing woman, Ecole des Beaux-Arts; Lugt 1950, no. 13, Pl. II. [4] Sitting young man, signed 'G. Berckheyde', Berlin, Kupferstichkabinett, catalogue Bock-Rosenberg 1930, no. 315. [5] Catalogue Almelo 1961, nos. 2–13.

8. Nicolaas Berchem, *Landscape with Icarus' fall* p. 47

DATA: Pen and bistre, bistre wash, on white paper 154 x 234 mm. Recto, at the foot: 'Berchem', owner's mark Esdaile (Lugt 2617). Verso: owner's mark Dimsdale (Lugt 2426), 'W. Esdaile 1883', '1833 WE out of dimsdale's colln., 25** Berghem'. Watermark no. 2.
LITERATURE: Hirschmann, p. 210. Becker, no 4*; Von Sick, p. 54, no. 28.

8. Nicolaas Berchem, *Landscape with Icarus' fall*

EXHIBITIONS: Leiden 1916C, no. 8; The Hague 1930, I no. 28; Groningen 1931, no. 34; Groningen 1948, no. 87; Groningen 1952, no. 8; The Hague 1955, no. 11; Ingelheim 1964, no. 11*.

PROVENANCE: Sale De Jongh Azn., Rotterdam 26.3.1810, Kbk D no. 4 (L. 7739); — Coll. Dimsdale; — Art dealer Woodburn; — Coll. Lawrence; — Art dealer Woodburn. Sale Esdaile, London 18.6.1840, no. 780 (L. 15865); Sale Knowles, London (Christie) 27.5.1908, no. 51; — Art dealer Colnaghi, London 1910; — Collection Hofstede de Groot, inv. no. 363, bequest 1914, no.8; — Groninger Museum voor Stad en Lande, inv. no. 1931–133.

Fig. 3. Nic. Berchem, *Phaeton's fall.* Drawing, Art dealer C. G. Boerner, Düsseldorf

The theme of this drawing,[1] not as popular in the middle of the seventeenth century as it had been in the years before and around 1600, seems to have the same function here as it had with the late mannerists: it allowed the artist to indulge in his beloved dream of a wide and peaceful landscape, lying far away in the past, untroubled by the worries of his own time. Soon after the moralistic lesson of Pieter Brueghel's famous Icarus, the theme acquired essentially the same purport as it had with Berchem. The plowing farmer, still depicted by Hans Bol, has disappeared here. In most cases Berchem no longer needed the pretext of mythology to enchant himself and his patrons with his sweeping view of Italy's warm soil.

Our drawing was sold together with its companion piece[2] (see fig. 3), a landscape with Phaëton's fall, dated 1665, at the De Jongh and Esdaile sales. Here the two drawings were catalogued as companion pieces with the same dimensions and technique. As the style of our drawing does not lead us to think otherwise, we may assume the same date of 1665 for Icarus' fall. We do not know of other versions of the theme by Berchem.

[1] Ovid, *Metamorphoses* VIII, 183–235. [2] Reproduced in: Neue Lagerliste 44 (1966), no. 8*, C. G. Boerner, Düsseldorf.

9. Job Berckheyde?, *Standing soldier* p. 139

DATA: Black chalk, on grey prepared paper 303 x 162 mm. Verso: italian landscape with travelers and horses near a fountain (black chalk), and 'no. 2382' (brown ink, see Lugt 2987). Watermark no. 3.

LITERATURE: Hirschmann, p. 209.

EXHIBITIONS: Leiden 1916C, no. 9; The Hague 1930, I no. 29; Groningen 1931, no. 35.

PROVENANCE: Sale Goll van Franckenstein, Amsterdam 1.7.1833. Kbk P. no. 29? (L. 13362); Sale Della Faille Waerloos, Amsterdam 19.1.1904, no. 23; — Collection Hofstede de Groot, inv. no. 242, bequest 1914, no. 9; — Groninger Museum voor Stad en Lande, inv. no. 1931–134.

Both sides of the sheet show a skilful hand, and probably the only thing that is needed to arrive at a definite attribution is the publication of documented comparable works.

Fig. 4. Job Berckheyde?, *Italian landscape with travellers and horses near a fountain.*
Drawing in black chalk, verso of cat. no. 9

The drawing has been attributed to Job Berckheyde although in his oeuvre, as far as is known, no link has been found. We prefer to maintain, with a certain reservation, the attribution to Berckheyde, as in a number of old auction catalogues[1] several studies of soldiers in the same technique are mentioned under the name of this artist.

The uniform of the soldier does not seem to belong to one of the regular regiments: 'Il disegno molto probabilmente riproduce un mercenario, cioè uno di quei soldati di ventura che, proprio nel sec. XVII, combatterono su tutti i territori d'Europa, al servizio di diversi stati, e che si vestivano come potevano, senza alcuna disciplina'.[2]

[1] Sale Amsterdam 27.11.1820, nos. 43 and 44: 'a seated soldier, black chalk (J. Berckheyde)'; sale Amsterdam 20.11.1843, no. 10: 'two pieces with soldiers, by J. Berckheyden'; sale Goll van Franckenstein, Amsterdam 1.7.1833, Kbk P no. 29: 'two pieces with soldiers, with black chalk, by Berckheyden'. One of these two last drawings, however, could have been the present one, as indicated by the owner's mark in verso. [2] Il Gen. di C. A. Arnaldo Forgiero, Director of the Museo Nazionale di Castel S. Angelo, Roma, kindly informed us about the military aspects of the drawing.

10. Jan de Bisschop, *View on the 'Valkenbergh' at Breda*   p. 53

DATA: Pen and bistre, bistre, grey and violet wash, on white paper 210 x 334 mm. Verso: two small pieces of paper pasted on the back, with 'Breda en Valkenbergh 15 jul. 1665' and '15 Jul. 1665. In Breda in 't Valkenbergh'; owner's mark Ploos van Amstel (Lugt 2726) with 'no. 1146'; 'no. 889' (see Lugt 2987). Watermark no. 4.

LITERATURE: Hirschmann, p. 211; Becker 1923, no. 5*; Hofstede de Groot 1914, p. 581; Bernt I, no. 67*.

EXHIBITIONS: The Hague 1902, no. 2; Groningen 1915, no. 22; Leiden 1916C, no. 13; The Hague 1930, I no. 32; Groningen 1931, no. 38; Breda 1952, no. 188*; The Hague 1955, no. 13.

PROVENANCE: Sale Tonneman, Amsterdam 21.10.1754, no. M64 (L. 845); — Sale Tolling, Amsterdam 21.11.1768, no. A11 (L. 1719); — Sale Van der Marck, Amsterdam 29.11.1773, no. 358 (L. 2206); — Sale Ploos van Amstel, Amsterdam 3.3.1800, no. E6 (L. 6031); — Sale Molkenboer, Amsterdam 17.10.1825, no. A29 (L. 10978); — Sale Goll van Franckenstein, Amsterdam 1.7.1833, Kbk A no. 29 (L. 13362); — Sale Van Cranenburgh, Amsterdam 26.10.1858, no. A17 (L. 24436); — Collection C. Kneppelhout van Sterkenburg, 1899; — Collection Hofstede de Groot, inv. no. 63, bequest 1914, no. 12; — Groninger Museum voor Stad en Lande, inv. no. 1931–137.

This good example of topographical drawing is documented by two inscriptions in verso. In Berlin[1] there is another view of the gardens of the castle at Breda with the tower of the old church in the distance, inscribed: 'Breda int Valkenbergh 14 jul. 1665' along with an undoubtedly apocryphal signature (see figure 5). The watermark of both drawings is the same, viz. a crowned flower-de-luce. In later times our drawing may have been slightly washed in another colour, although there is in Brussels[2] a large panoramic view of The Hague, executed at the same time, showing the same combination of bistre and violet wash.

Fig. 5. Jan de Bisschop, *View of the 'Valkenbergh' at Breda*. Drawing, Berlin, Kupferstichkabinett

Confusion with De Bisschop's and Huygens' drawings has always presented a difficulty which still awaits a definite solution. We can trace our drawing in the catalogues of different auction-sales back to the Tonneman sale in 1754. About twenty drawings by De Bisschop were in this collection, among which figured also the view of The Hague, mentioned above (no.

M60). Most of the drawings by Constantijn Huygens were sold at the Stinstra sale.[3] Also, according to Hofstede de Groot's catalogue of Huygens's drawings in Thieme-Becker's *Lexikon*[4] most of his drawings were executed between 1669 and 1680. It is therefore, in this case, hardly necessary to enter into a stylistic or graphological discussion concerning the drawings of the artists.

[1] Kupferstichkabinett, cat. Bock-Rosenberg 1930, no. 5853*. [2] Collection De Grez, cat. 1913, no. 1753, as Constantijn Huygens; inscription: 'van Haagschen Toren, 4 jun. 1665.' At exh. Vancouver 1958 no. 7*, as J. de Bisschop. [3] Sale J. Stinstra a.o., Amsterdam 17.2.1823. [4] Huygens, Constantin d. J., (mit Notizen von C. Hofstede de Groot), in: *Allgemeines Lexikon der bildenden Künstler . . .* begründet von Ulrich Thieme und Felix Becker, XVIII, Leipzig 1925, p. 198/9.

11. Jan de Bisschop, *Study of two women peeling apples*   p. 140

DATA: Pen and bistre, bistre wash, on white paper 176 x 270 mm. Recto, upper right side, pen and brown ink: '16 Sept. 1668'. Verso: '16 Sept. 1668', 'coll. A. G. de Visser n. 28 Amsterdam Mai 1881', owner's mark Von Lanna (Lugt 2773). Watermark no. 5.

LITERATURE: Van Regteren Altena 1931, p. 75*.

EXHIBITIONS: Leiden 1916C, no. 14; The Hague 1930, I no. 33; Groningen 1931, no. 39; Groningen 1952, no. 10; The Hague 1955, no. 14.

PROVENANCE: Sale Van Huls, The Hague 14.5.1736, no. 1686? (L. 464); — Sale Neyman, Paris 8.7.1776, no. 70? (L. 2566); Sale De Visser, Amsterdam 16.5.1881, no. 28 (L. 41110); Sale Von Lanna, Stuttgart 6.5.1910, no. 93; — Collection Hofstede de Groot, inv. no. 365, bequest 1914, no.13; — Groninger Museum voor Stad en Lande, inv. no. 1931–138.

This drawing could be the same one which figured in sale S. van Huls,[1] when a collection of about hundred drawings by Bisschop was sold. Also at sale Neyman[2] there was 'une petite étude de deux femmes assises, au bistre.' In Rotterdam[3] there is a small drawing of a sitting woman, seen from the rear and attributed to Cornelis Bisschop, not unlike the present study.

[1] The Hague 14.5.1736, no. 1686: 'deux femmes assises, et 5 autres'. [2] Paris 8.7.1776, no. 70. [3] Museum Boymans-van Beuningen, inv. no. CDBI.

12. Anthonie van Borssum?, *Landing-stage and a pollard willow*   p. 141

DATA: pen and bistre, on white paper 105 x 178 mm. Watermark Amsterdam arms; not in Churchill.

LITERATURE: Schneider, no. Z191.

EXHIBITIONS: Groningen 1915, no. 37; Leiden 1916C, no. 68; The Hague 1930, I no. 72; Groningen 1931, no. 77; Vancouver 1958, no. 46.

PROVENANCE: Sale F. A. v. S., Amsterdam 11.6.1912, no. 150; — Collection Hofstede de Groot, inv. no. 496, bequest 1914, no. 44; — Groninger Museum voor Stad en Lande, inv. no. 1931–176.

Schneider (see Bibliography) incorporated the drawing in the oeuvre of Lievens as being undoubtedly authentic. It is not easy, however, to find any close resemblance of form among the documented or generally accepted work of the artist. The disorderly aspect of the composition is not in accordance with Lievens' flowing organization of space. Also the drawing has a dry conciseness quite different from the decorative effect of Lievens' pen strokes.

To judge by some of the details (a.o. the drawing of the landingstage and the figures), Professor Van Regteren Altena's suggestion of Anthonie van Borssum's name seems plausible, the more so because there has often been confusion between the work of the two artists.

13. Leendert van der Cooghen, *Study of the head of a boy*   p. 142

DATA: Black chalk, on white paper 237 x 192 mm. Verso: owner's mark K. E. von Liphart (Lugt 1687).
LITERATURE: Henkel 1916, p. 343; Hirschmann, p. 407*; Frerichs 1956, p. 17.
EXHIBITIONS: Leiden 1916A, no. 37; The Hague 1930, I no. 36; Groningen 1931, no. 42; The Hague 1955, no. 16.
PROVENANCE: Sale Von Liphart, Leipzig 26.4.1898 no. 539 (L. 56238); — Sale F. A. v. S., Amsterdam 11.6.1912, no. 371*; — Collection Hofstede de Groot, inv. no. 489, bequest 1914, no. 19; — Groninger Museum voor Stad en Lande, inv. no. 1931–141.

There are several signed drawings[1] by the amateur draughtsman Leendert van der Cooghen which give us an idea of his style and technique. His favourite subject is portraiture, in which he manages to express a certain sensitiveness. The tender and respectful intentness of the draughtsman towards his model make this drawing one of the best examples of Van der Cooghen's work, comparable to a drawing formerly also in the collection Hofstede de Groot.[2]

[1] Portrait of a boy, formerly collection Hofstede de Groot, auction-sale Leipzig (Boerner) 4.11.1931 no. 43; portrait of a man, formerly collection Grand Duchess of Weimar, photo Braun no. 79560; portrait of a woman, collection Liechtenstein, Vienna, no. 47; portrait of a woman, Berlin, Kupferstichkabinett, cat. Bock-Rosenberg 1930, no. 2876.   [2] Reproduced in Becker, *Neue Folge* no. 7; Magazine catalogue Boerner, 1918, no. 108.

14. Albert Cuyp, *Landscape near Calcar, with the Monterenberg in the distance*   p. 143

DATA: Black chalk, grey wash, on white paper 139 x 239 mm. Recto, lower left corner, in brown ink: 'A. Cuijp'. Verso, in black chalk: sketch of a river and a distant bank with two sailing boats; owner's mark Heseltine (Lugt 1507). Watermark no. 6.
LITERATURE: Henkel 1916, p. 341; Dattenberg p. 43; Gorissen no. 20.
EXHIBITIONS: Leiden 1916A, no. 42; The Hague 1930, I no. 41; Groningen 1931, no. 47; Groningen 1952, no. 24*; Düsseldorf 1953, no. 20*; The Hague 1955, no. 19; Vancouver 1958, no. 18*.
PROVENANCE: Sale Cook, London 1.6.1857, no. 117 (L. 23659); Sale Heseltine, Amsterdam 27.5.1913, no. 79*; — Collection Hofstede de Groot, inv. no. 526, bequest 1914, no. 24; — Groninger Museum voor Stad en Lande, inv. no. 1931–146.

Together with two similar landscapes of the same subject, our drawing figured at sale Heseltine.[1] At sale Huldschinsky[2] there was a drawing of the Monterenberg and Calcar with the same watermark as ours. Also there exist several paintings by Cuyp with a view on the same place.[3]

10. Jan de Bisschop, *View on the 'Valkenbergh' at Breda*

In verso, there is a sketch in black chalk of a river with two sailing boats, with hills beyond the further bank (see fig. 6).

[1] Amsterdam 27.5.1913, no. 78: view on the Monterenberg from the opposite side as on our drawing, now in Berlin, Kupferstichkabinett, cat. 1930, no. 6561; the same sale, no. 80; view on Elten, now in coll. F. Lugt, inv. no. 5304.   [2] Berlin 3.11.1931, no. 27, exh. Brussels 1937–38, no. 54.   [3] (1) Sale Sécrétan, Paris 1.7.1889, no. 107, afterwards coll. Havemeyer, New York. (2) Coll. Lord Carlisle, Castle Howard, Dulwich, Hofstede de Groot 1907–28, II, no. 71. In *Burlington Magazine* 1953, p. 34, Prof. Van Gelder described this painting as a reverse copy by A. Calraet after Cuyp's painting in the coll. of the Duke of Bedford, mentioned hereafter. (3) Coll. Duke of Bedford, Hofstede de Groot 1907–28, II, no. 72.

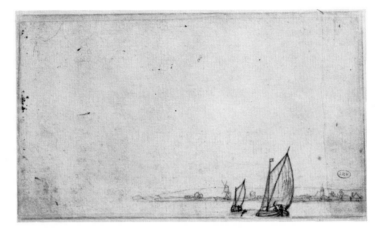

Fig. 6. Albert Cuyp, *Sketch of a river and a distant bank.* Drawing in black chalk, verso of cat. no. 14

15. Albert Cuyp, *View of a wide landscape* p. 144

DATA: Black chalk, grey wash, on white paper 185 x 484 mm. Recto, pen and brown ink, lower left corner: 'A. Kuip'. Watermark no. 6.

EXHIBITIONS: Leiden 1916A, no. 43; The Hague 1930, I no. 37; Groningen 1931, no. 43; Groningen 1948, no. 93; Groningen 1952, no. 20.

PROVENANCE: Coll. Palmerston; Sale Sir James Knowles, London (Christie) 27.5.1908, no. 57; — Collection Hofstede de Groot, inv. no. 385, bequest 1914, no. 20; — Groninger Museum voor Stad en Lande, inv. no. 1931–142.

This must be one of Cuyp's landscape drawings, retouched in the eighteenth century. In numerous sale catalogues we can find copies of Cuyp or drawings by Cuyp worked over by artists such as A. van Strij and A. Schouman. In the lead-pencil drawing underneath we seem to recognize Cuyp's hand, but the heavy wash must have been executed by one of these later artists. From other drawings by Schouman[1] we are familiar with the way in which the little dots in the right foreground and the clouds are washed in.

In the catalogue of the auction sale of Schouman's collection[2] we find two entries mentioning twelve pieces by Cuyp, 'several views, washed'. It may well be that our drawing figured among these twelve.

In the Palmerston collection it was included with a companion piece, which afterwards appeared at sale Duval, Amsterdam 22.6.1910, no. 83.

[¹] 'De pastory van 's-Gravesande', private collection, Zeist, signed and dated; 'Het dorp Monster', Amsterdam, Rijksprentenkabinet, inv. no. 4386, monogram and date.   [²] The Hague 10.12.1792, nos. 914 and 917.

16. Albert Cuyp, *Study of a reclining shepherd boy* p. 145

DATA: Black chalk, black ink, grey wash, on white paper 85 x 103 mm. Recto, upper left corner: owner's mark Esdaile (Lugt 2617). Verso, at the foot: 'WE-1807-Trowards collection P 35 N 311 A Cuyp', owner's mark Bale (Lugt 640).

LITERATURE: Henkel 1916, p. 342.

EXHIBITIONS: Leiden 1916A, no. 39; The Hague 1930, I no 38; Groningen 1931, no. 44; Groningen 1948, no. 92; Groningen 1952, no. 21; The Hague 1955, no. 18.

PROVENANCE: Coll. Troward; — Sale Esdaile, London (Christie) 18.6.1840, no. 908 (L. 15865); Sale Bale, London (Christie) 9.6.1881, no. 2275 (L. 41193); Sale Knowles, London 27.5.1908, 56; — Collection Hofstede de Groot, inv. no. 387, bequest 1914, no. 21; — Groninger Museum voor Stad en Lande, inv. 1931–144.

There are two versions of a similar study of resting shepherd boys,¹ which resemble our drawing very closely (see fig. 7). The reclining boy in the present study we find repeated in several paintings, e.g. in the collection van Heel, Rijssen² and in New York, Metropolitan Museum.³

[¹] (1) Amsterdam, Rijksprentenkabinet, inv. no. A3075, reproduced in *Beeldende Kunst* III, 1916, no. 35. (2) Vorden, coll. Jhr. Mr. Victor de Stuers, cat. 1961, no. 51.   [²] Exh. Almelo 1953, no. 11 and Rotterdam 1955, no. 57*.   [³] Hofstede de Groot 1907–28, II, no. 211, cat. Metropolitain Museum 1931, no. 99–1.

Fig. 7. Albert Cuyp, *Studies of resting shepherd boys*. Drawing,
Amsterdam, Rijksprentenkabinet

17. Albert Cuyp, *Study of a cow*

p. 146

DATA: Black chalk, black ink, grey wash, on white paper 72 x 136 mm, pasted on white paper. Recto, lower right corner: owner's mark Esdaile (Lugt 2617). Verso, at the foot: 'WE-1807-Trowards collection P 35 N 431 A Cuyp', owner's mark Bale (Lugt 640).

LITERATURE: Henkel 1916, p. 342.

EXHIBITIONS: Leiden 1916A, no. 40; The Hague 1930, I no. 40; Groningen 1931, no. 45; Groningen 1948, no. 91; Groningen 1952, no. 22; The Hague 1955, no. 17.

PROVENANCE: Coll. Troward; — Sale Esdaile, London (Christie) 18.6.1840, no. 908 (L. 15865); — Sale Bale, London (Christie) 9.6.1881, no. 2275 (L. 41193); — Sale Knowles, London 27.5.1908, no. 56; — Collection Hofstede de Groot, inv. no. 388, bequest 1914, no. 22; — Groninger Museum voor Stad en Lande, inv. no. 1931–144.

An important study, certainly by Cuyp's own hand, which shows his ability as a draughtsman. The cow in this study recurs in a number of paintings, e.g. Hofstede de Groot 1907–28, II, no. 194, coll. Sir Edmond Bacon, Raveningham Hall, Norwich. Hofstede de Groot 1907–28, II, no. 212 = 302, Frick collection, New York, cat. 1945, no. 28 (in reverse). Hofstede de Groot 1907–28, II, no. 217, New York, Metropolitan Museum, cat. no. C99–3 (in reverse). Hofstede de Groot 1907–28, II, no. 330, London, Dulwich College, cat. 1953, no. 128 (in reverse). Hofstede de Groot 1907–28 II, no. 335, New York, Gallery Knoedler, repr. in *Pantheon* III, 1929, p. 53. Hofstede de Groot 1907–28, II, no. 429, London, National Gallery, inv. no. 1289.

18. Copy after Albert Cuyp, *Studies of a cow and a calf*

p. 147

DATA: Black chalk, black ink, grey wash, on white paper 91 x 153 mm.

LITERATURE: Henkel 1916, p. 342.

EXHIBITIONS: Leiden 1916A, no. 41; The Hague 1930, I no. 39; Groningen 1931, no. 46; Groningen 1952, no. 23.

Fig. 8. Albert Cuyp, *Study of two cows*. Drawing, Amsterdam, Rijksprentenkabinet

PROVENANCE: Sale Knowles, London 27.5.1908, no. 56; — Collection Hofstede de Groot, inv. no. 389, bequest 1914, no. 23; — Groninger Museum voor Stad en Lande, inv. no. 1931–145.

In the Printroom of the Rijksmuseum in Amsterdam[1] there is a similar study with a standing and a lying cow in the same position (see fig. 8). In spite of slight differences, we must assume that there is a connection between the two drawings.

The Amsterdam study recurs in several paintings,[2] whereas our drawing has not been used by Cuyp. We must therefore assume the possibility of our drawing being a copy. Also the quality of our study is inferior to that in Amsterdam. The dividing line between animal and grass is harshly drawn; the heavy outlines are also characteristic of a copy.

[1] Inv. no. '62:79. Sale Amsterdam 22.3.1802, no. 14. This drawing has a counterpart in a study in Berlin of a standing and a lying cow; cat. Bock/Rosenberg, 1930, no. 10345. Both drawings a refrom the Barnard collection. [2] Hofstede de Groot, 1907–28, II, no. 189, sale London, 14.5.1926; Hofstede de Groot 1907–28, II, no. 557, Mainz, Gemälde Galerie, inv. no. 719, cat. 1911, no. 145a.

19. Lambert Doomer, *Wicket in a fence* p. 148

DATA: Pen and bistre, grey and bistre wash, on white paper 210 x 281 mm. Verso: owner's mark Waal (Lugt 2541). Watermark no. 7.
LITERATURE: Hirschmann, p. 206.
EXHIBITIONS: Groningen 1915, no. 23; Leiden 1916c, no. 42; The Hague 1930, I no. 42; Groningen 1931, no. 48; Groningen 1952, no. 25; The Hague 1955, no. 20.
PROVENANCE: Collection G. Waal, Edam 1906; — Collection Hofstede de Groot, inv. no. 287, bequest 1914, no. 25; — Groninger Museum voor Stad en Lande, inv. no. 1931–147.

The drawings of Lambert Doomer, a draughtsman of high quality, generally depict landscapes with a marked topographical tendency. A great number of views of Nantes and its neighbourhood is preserved in various collections. Our drawing seems to belong to Doomer's pure landscape drawings without topographical interest, occurring less often, and may have been executed in the artist's later years which he spent in Alkmaar. Hofstede de Groot acquired the drawing from G. Waal, Edam.[1]

[1] See Lugt, p. 476, no. 2541. See also this catalogue, p. 34.

20. Egbert van Drielst, *View in the woodland of Eext* p. 149

DATA: Black chalk, grey wash, on white paper 300 x 425 mm. Verso, pen and brown ink: 'in de Eext op het Landschap Drente E. van Drielst'.
EXHIBITIONS: Groningen 1915, no. 24; The Hague 1930, I no. 43; Groningen 1931, no. 49.
PROVENANCE: Sale Berlin 25.5.1908, no. 154; — Collection Hofstede de Groot, inv. no. 395, bequest 1914, no. 26; — Groninger Museum voor Stad en Lande, inv. no. 1931–148.

Van Drielst, the author of numerous pleasant and sometimes even brilliantly drawn landscapes, executed a number of views in the village of Eext, in the province of Drenthe, dated from 1780 to 1806.

22. Allaert van Everdingen, *Hilly landscape with a church to the left*

The spiritual content of his landscapes shows a distinct development comparable to the change from the gay and careless summer landscapes of Rococo to the more austere atmosphere of later, troubled times. The artist often annotated the drawings in verso in his characteristic handwriting, as he has done in this case. Our landscape must have been executed in the last five years of the eighteenth century.[1]

[1] For the information regarding the chronology of Van Drielst's work we are indebted to J. W. Niemeijer, Rijksprentenkabinet, Amsterdam.

21. Cornelis Dusart, *The feast of St.Nikolaas* p. 150

DATA: Pen and bistre, bistre wash, on white paper 246 x 203 mm, pasted on paper. Verso, in brown ink: 'N. 70/Cornelis Dusart b: at Haerlem 1665. D: 1704-', owner's mark Roupell (Lugt 2234).

LITERATURE: Hirschmann, p. 210; Becker, *Neue Folge*, no. 11.

EXHIBITIONS: The Hague 1902, no. 19; Leiden 1903, no. 145; Leiden 1916C, no. 45; The Hague 1930, I no. 44; Groningen 1931, no. 50; Groningen 1952, no. 28; The Hague 1955, no. 21.

PROVENANCE: Sale Stadnitsky and Muller, Amsterdam 16.5.1831 Omslag B no. 60? (L. 12669); Sale Roupell, London (Christie) 12.7.1887, no. 1158 (L. 46748); Art dealer Wawra, Vienna 1902; — Collection Hofstede de Groot, inv. no. 124, bequest 1914, no. 27; — Groninger Museum voor Stad en Lande, inv. no. 1931–149.

In addition to our drawing there were at least two other versions of the theme, in watercolour.[1] Roupell probably bought the drawing in London, as there is in verso an inscription in English in an early nineteenth century hand. An entry in the catalogue of sale Stadnitsky and Muller[2] could possibly apply to our drawing.

[1] Sale Amsterdam 2.3.1829, no. 13: 'De St. Nicolaasdag, geestig voorgesteld door C. Dusart. Gekleurd.' Exposition Leeds, 1886, no. 2582: 'St. Nicholas' Day in Holland, composition of many figures. Highly finished in water colours. From the Esdaile and Robinson collections, J. Malcolm Esq.' [2] 'Eene Sint Nicolaasvreugd, door C. Dusart.'

22. Allaert van Everdingen, *Hilly landscape with a church to the left* p. 58

DATA: Aquarelle, on white paper 184 x 308 mm. Recto, on the trunk in the middle foreground: 'A.V.E.'. Watermark no. 8.

LITERATURE: Hirschmann, p. 210.

EXHIBITIONS: Groningen 1915, no. 28; Leiden 1916C, no. 49; The Hague 1930, I no. 48; Groningen 1931, no. 54; Groningen 1952, no. 31; The Hague 1955, no. 22.

PROVENANCE: Sale Mendes de Leon, Amsterdam 20.11.1843, Kbk D no. 4 (L. 17148); — Sale H. de Kat, Rotterdam 4.3.1867, no. 110 (L. 29574); Art dealer Fr. Muller, Amsterdam 1906; — Collection Hofstede de Groot, inv. no. 311, bequest 1914, no. 31; — Groninger Museum voor Stad en Lande, inv. no. 1931–153.

The decorative quality of this watercolour far exceeds its merits as a composition. When we see the magnificent execution, however, no doubt about the authorship exists. Professor Van de

Waal suggested the possibility that our drawing belonged to the artist's later period, as indicated by the weary, almost mechanical way in which the elements of the composition are put together. There is an enormous difference indeed from the vigorous composition of Everdingen's earlier, northern mountain landscapes. Similar views in or near small villages are to be found in London,[1] Leiden,[2] Berlin[3] and Paris.[4]

[1] British Museum, cat. Hind, III, 1926, p. 91, no. 35.   [2] Prentenkabinet der Rijksuniversiteit, inv. no. 244. [3] Coll. Dr W. Beck, Berlin-Friedenau, formerly Leningrad, Eremitage, sale Boerner, 29.4.1931, no. 68.   [4] Coll. F. Lugt, inv. no. 2648.

23, 24. Contre-épreuves after Allaert van Everdingen, *Two northern landscapes* p. 152, 153

DATA: Sanguine, black chalk, grey wash, on white paper 103 x 158 mm. No. 1931–151 signed on the rock, under the draughtsmen: 'A.VE'.

LITERATURE: Hirschmann, p. 210.

EXHIBITIONS: Groningen 1915, nos. 26 and 27; Leiden 1916C, nos. 47 and 48; The Hague 1930, I nos. 46 and 47; Groningen 1931, nos. 52 and 53.

Figs. 9, 10. Allaert van Everdingen, *Two northern landscapes*. Etchings, Bartsch 58 and Bartsch 63

PROVENANCE: Sale De Jongh Azn., Rotterdam 26.3.1810, nos. H4 and H5 (?) (L. 7739); Sale Strauss, Wien 2.5.1906, nos. 36 and 37; — Collection Hofstede de Groot, inv. nos. 268 and 269, bequest 1914, nos. 29 and 30; — Groninger Museum voor Stad en Lande, inv. nos. 1931–151 and 1931–152.

We find these landscapes in reverse on two etchings by Everdingen (Bartsch 58 and 63). Yet the drawings are not the original studies for the etchings, but probably eighteenth century contre-épreuves. The forger has extended the drawings a little beyond the margin of the etchings. This margin, however, is still visible on both drawings. We can even see the plate mark in the lower left corner of the drawing with the sailing boats. Also, in the lines of the clouds we can clearly see that the drawings are contre-épreuves. Only the sanguine has been counter-printed, directly from a sanguine-sketch made upon the etchings. The black chalk and the grey wash have been applied afterwards. Two similar contre-épreuves in the same technique, though a little smaller than ours, are in Teyler's Museum, Haarlem (inv. nos. Q36 and Q37), counter-prints from Everdingen's etchings Bartsch 14 and 40.

25. Jacques de Gheyn II, *Portrait in miniature of George Clifford, third Earl of Cumberland* p. 151

DATA: Silverpoint on yellow prepared vellum 67 x 54 mm, octagonal. Verso: owner's mark Von Lanna (Lugt 2773) and '171'.

LITERATURE: Hirschmann, p. 406; Van Regteren Altena 1931, p. 71; Van Regteren Altena 1948, no. 7a.

EXHIBITIONS: Groningen 1915, no. 30; Groningen 1931, no. 55; The Hague 1930, I no. 49.

PROVENANCE: Sale Von Lanna, Stuttgart 6.5.1910, no. 272; — Collection Hofstede de Groot, inv. no. 402, bequest 1914, no. 33; — Groninger Museum voor Stad en Lande, inv. no. 1931–145.

This beautiful portrait was catalogued as Goltzius at the Von Lanna sale and no identification was given. Because of the numerous unidentified portraits by De Gheyn and Goltzius occurring in old auction catalogues it is not possible to arrive at any conclusion concerning the provenance. Two similar miniatures formerly listed as Goltzius, were attributed to De Gheyn by E. K. J. Reznicek.[1]

In 1594 De Gheyn did an engraved portrait, the silver plate of which is preserved in the British Museum.[2] This plate bears the inscription 'Jacques de Gheyn fe. in London' in verso. Dr. Bierens de Haan read the monogram at the bottom as 'non sine Deo' and identified the sitter as George Clifford, third Earl of Cumberland.

We were struck by the similarity of the man in this engraving and the man in our miniature. There exist some other documented portraits of Cumberland. Magda and Willem de Passe depicted the naval commander in Holland's *Herωologia*.[3] Nicholas Hilliard painted two miniatures, one of which is in Kansas City[4] and the other in the National Maritime Museum.[5] Thomas Cockson also engraved a portrait of Cumberland[6] probably in the winter of 1598–99 just after the most momentous of the Earl's expeditions.[7] At about the same time, William Rogers executed an engraved portrait of the famous nautical Quixote.[8] Notwithstanding this wealth of comparative material it is not easy to arrive at a definite conclusion. Most of the artists appear to modify their model according to the prevalent standards of portraiture. As these standards were rather formal, only the very great artists succeeded in conveying a certain amount of reality, in the modern sense of the word. When Dr Whitaker in 1803 examined the body of the Earl in the family vault at Skipton in Craven he found that 'all the painters had the complaisance to omit three large warts upon the left cheek'.[9] We are therefore forced to judge by rather general characteristics of physiognomy. In most of the abovementioned portraits the man looks quite different, although the individual features are similar. We find the hollow-eyed look in all the portraits; the thick curly hair recedes from the high forehead, and falls in long locks on the neck. The shape and poise of the head in the

Fig. 11. Jacques de Gheyn II, *Portrait of George Clifford, third Earl of Cumberland.*
Etching.

various portraits are not dissimilar. As the English portraits, however, have been executed by rather out-moded artists, the comparison chiefly shows us the difference in conception with which De Gheyn executed his portrait. This difference is so great that we might think we are looking at two different men: the old-fashioned, romantic-looking knight of Chivalry, and the cold-blooded, debauched buccaneer. De Gheyn, probably not having seen the already existing portraits of Cumberland, has been able to give a totally new 'image' of the earl. As the English portraits do not make our identification impossible, we may, relying on the engraved portrait of Cumberland by De Gheyn, assume that the sitter of our drawing was indeed Cumberland. Also the likeness of the portraits in the *Herωologia* and the present drawing is so convincing as to leave hardly any room for doubt. The drawing may have been made as a study for the engraving; in that case it can be dated 1594. There is a curious discrepancy between the body and the head with the collar in our portrait. The upper part is obviously a study after nature, whereas the body seems a shapeless form which is not convincing at all. We may even assume that a later hand was responsible for the weak drawing of the body. Here we see a typical example of the methods used in portraiture of the time. The artists treated the head and the body, mostly displaying of military costume or court dress, as quite different entities. Frans Floris and Cornelis Ketel are known to have used this procedure also. There are two costume-sketches by Ketel, in which the faces are not filled in. These studies may have been executed in the same years as our portrait.[10]

Cumberland has been represented as a courtier, gambler and buccaneer: 'His love of adventure was strong, and he staked his money on the success of his cruisers in much the same spirit that he did on the speed of his horses or the turn of his dice. And he spared his body no more than his purse. His courage was unimpeachable, and the temper which he showed in times of difficulty won him both credit and popularity. At court he was in high favour with the Queen, whose glove, set in diamonds, he wore as a plume in his hat. He is described as a man of great personal beauty, strong and active, accomplished in all knightly exercises, splendid in his dress, and of romantic valour. On the other hand, he was a gambler and a spendthrift, a faithless husband and for several years before his death was separated from his wife'.[11]

[1] Reznicek I, p. 484. Berlin, Kupferstichkabinett, inv. nos. 6833 and 4456. We are also indebted to Professor Reznicek for other facts and insights concerning the De Gheyn drawings, imparted in the course of conversation. [2] Dept. of Coins and Medals, Gift Okeover, 1920. Hollstein VII p. 165, no. 321 II. Dated in the border-inscription 1594. Note also the earrings which the man is wearing in both cases. See fig. 11. [3] Henry Holland, *Herωologia*, London 1620, illustrated by Magda and Willem de Passe. Cumberland's portrait appears on p. 121. [4] Nelson Gallery no. F58–60/188, repr. in *Handbook* 1959, Auerbach, no. 88. [5] Ex Buccleuch collection, Cat. exh. Hilliard, London 1947, no. 54; H. A. Kennedy, *Buccleuch Miniatures*, 1917, Pl. 17; C. Winter, *Elizabethan Miniatures*, 1943, Pl. 5; special number of *The Studio*, 1917, Pl. XVII; Auerbach, no. 87. [6] Reproduced in A. M. Hind, *Engraving in England*, I (Tudor) no. 7, p. 243, Pl. 125. [7] It is interesting to note that in 1598 Chrispijn de Passe made an engraved portrait of Sir Francis Drake (Franken no. 561). [8] A. M. Hind, *Engraving in England*, I (Tudor) no. 4, p. 262, Pl. 138. [9] Quotation taken from the *Dictionary of National Biography*, Vol. XI, p. 60. [10] See J. Richard Judson in *Master Drawings* I, 1963, 4, p. 38 and Pl. 26 and 27. [11] *Dictionary of National Biography*, Vol. XI, p. 61.

26. Jacques de Gheyn II, *A blowing trumpeter* p. 67

DATA: Pen and bistre, grey wash, on greyish paper 147 x 157 mm. Verso: signed in a later hand 'J... de Gheyn f.' Watermark no. 9.

LITERATURE: Henkel 1916, p. 340; Van Regteren Altena 1931, p. 71; Van Regteren Altena 1935, p. 53, 83 and 84.

EXHIBITIONS: Groningen 1915, no. 32; Leiden 1916A, no. 45; The Hague 1930, I no. 50; Groningen 1931, no. 57; Groningen 1948, no. 94; Groningen 1952, no. 34*; Washington 1958, no. 32.

PROVENANCE: Sale D. Muilman, Amsterdam 29.3.1773, Kbk Q no. 1250 (L. 2149); — Sale Van Maarseveen, Amsterdam 28.10.1793, Kbk L no. 57 (L. 5115). — Sale Ploos van Amstel, Amsterdam 3.3.1800, Kbk X no. 52 (L. 6031); Sale Boreel, Amsterdam 15.6.1908, no. 211; — Sale F. A. v. S., Amsterdam 11.6.1912, no. 92; Art dealer Hoogendijk, Amsterdam — Collection Hofstede de Groot, inv. no. 490, bequest 1914, no. 35; — Groninger Museum voor Stad en Lande, inv. no. 1931–156.

There are a number of similar studies[1] for the set of twenty-two engravings of cavalry exercises (Hollstein VII, p. 140, nos. 263–284) executed in the years 1598–99. Being a draughtsman of the highest quality, De Gheyn is able to convey the impression that the trumpeter is on horseback without depicting the horse itself. We can imagine vividly how the man is trying to keep his impetuous horse under control with the reins that must be gathered into his left hand. Professor Reznicek drew our attention to the interesting question of the origin of the liberal and picturesque use of the wash. In Holland this technique was especially popular in The Hague, where De Gheyn probably introduced it. Some drawings, copies after antique sculptures, by Augustijn Terwesten the Elder, and the two drawings in this collection by the Hague artist Jan de Bisschop are a further example. De Gheyn's studies for the handbook of musketry exercises are also executed in this manner.

In most cases, when confronted with a question like this, we can safely turn to Italy in order to find the answer. Adam Elsheimer, a very important link between Holland and Italy, made a few pure brush drawings.[2] In general one can say that the Italian mannerists have set the example for their northern colleagues. We can see the growing importance of the heavy wash in drawings by Andrea Schiavone,[3] Federigo Barocci[4] and Federigo Zuccaro.[5] Also Gaudenzio Ferrari[6] and Lodovico Cardi (Cigoli)[7] made brush-drawings in which the line-drawing is reduced to a minimum. There is another Italian artist, however, Andrea Boscoli (ca. 1560–1607), who is known especially for his pure brush-drawings. The *Mostra di disegni di Andrea Boscoli,* Firenze 1959 (Gabinetto di disegni e stampe degli Uffizi, cat. no. XI) showed a number of drawings[8] that are very similar in technique.

Van Regteren Altena[9] has pointed out that De Gheyn must have known Tempesta's work in connection with his engravings for the cavalry exercises. In 1598 De Gheyn could have seen a number of engravings by Tempesta, representing battle scenes of military subjects.[10] Jacques de Gheyn III, the son, executed etchings after Tempesta's drawings.[11]

[1] Amsterdam, Rijksprentenkabinet; Paris, coll. F. Lugt; Paris, Louvre, see: Lugt 1929–33, Vol. I, nos. 277* and 278*; Vienna, Albertina, cat. Benesch, 1928, no. 390*, dated 1598; London, British Museum, cat. Hind, Vol. V, 1932, p. 158, no. 7; Rotterdam, Museum Boymans—Van Beuningen. [2] Budapest, Szépmüvészeti Múzeum; Hans Möhle, *Die Zeichnungen Adam Elsheimers,* Berlin 1966, Kat. no. D7*, as anonymous master. Inv. no. E. 27–23a. [3] Budapest, Szépmüvészeti Múzeum, cat. 1960 (*Velencei es egyeb eszakitaliai rajzok*) no. 17, Pl. no. 7. [4] Coll. Janos Scholz, New York. Exh. Köln 1963–64, no. 8, Pl. no. 32. [5] Coll. Van Regteren Altena, Amsterdam. Exh. Paris, Rotterdam, Haarlem 1962, no. 135, Pl. CI. [6] Coll. C. R. Rudolf, London. Exh. London, Birmingham, Leeds 1962, no. 21, Pl. 2. [7] Louvre, inv. no. 911 (copy in Windsor Castle, cat. 1949, no. 233, Pl. 41), Exh. Firenze 1959, no. 30, Tav. 30; Louvre, inv. no. 915, exh. Rome 1959, no. 33*. [8] Plates nos. 6, 7, 8, 23, 25, 27, 31, 32, 33 and 34. In the catalogue our attention is drawn to this technique (no. 89): 'tanto il Boscoli negli ultimi tempi si abandona felicemente al fluire della mano, che evoca sul bianco del fogli uno svariare continuo delle ombre, un molle arruffarsi delle linee pur rimanendo sensibile la consistenza della forma, nella sicurezza dei gesti, nel netto stagliarsi delle fronde.' And with another drawing (Lot and his daughters, no. 79): 'Si pensa al "giovane manierismo" olandese, specie per l'intrico puntuto, compleso, di linee e ombre sotto cui la forma si compone accidentata e vibrante, come in uno Spranger o in un Goltzius meno sfrenato e scabroso…' [9] See Bibliography Van Regteren Altena 1935. [10] Bartsch nos. 559 (1591), 596–607 (1596), 636 (1593). [11] Le Blanc nos. 2–11.

27. Jacques de Gheyn II, *Drinking fisherman, sitting on a basket*   p. 154

DATA : Pen and bistre, on white paper 203 x 155 mm. Verso, in brown ink, in a later hand: 'Jacq. de gheyn f. geb. 1565 h. 7 ¾ b. 6', owner's mark Von Lanna (Lugt 2773) with '482'. Watermark no. 10.

LITERATURE : Henkel 1916, p. 340; Van Regteren Altena 1931, p. 71; Van Regteren Altena 1935, p. 50.

EXHIBITIONS : Groningen 1915, no. 31; Leiden 1916A, no. 44; The Hague 1930, I no. 51; Groningen 1931, no. 56; Groningen 1952, no. 33; The Hague 1955, no. 23.

PROVENANCE: Sale Ploos van Amstel, Amsterdam 3.3.1800, Kbk DD no. 22 (L. 6031). — Sale Amsterdam 22.3.1802, Kbk R no. 54 (L. 6387); Sale Von Lanna, Stuttgart 6.5.1910, no. 262; — Collection Hofstede de Groot, inv. no. 405, bequest 1914, no. 34; — Groninger Museum voor Stad en Lande, inv. no. 1931–155.

Especially in the years around 1600, De Gheyn's style of drawing shows a marked development. Dated works from the period 1598–1600 are characterized by a certain restraint, expressing itself in stiff hatching, reminding us of the fact that he was also an engraver. The drawings from the year 1602 have a casual appearance, with a free and relaxed line. From 1603 onwards, De Gheyn's lines seem to acquire a nervous undulating quality, like weeds in a whirlpool. Our drawing fits in very well with other works of 1602 not only in style but also in subject matter. There are at least two other drawings[1] by De Gheyn representing scenes of fishermen, all dated 1602. De Gheyn's preoccupation with beach scenes is understandable, when we think of the engravings of the sailing-cart and of the fact that he lived in The Hague, near Scheveningen.

De Gheyn here precedes Goltzius[2] in representing fishermen and their *ambiente* as a pictorial genre. Traditionally linked with two different areas of spiritual thinking, the theme was depicted in the context both of the apostles and of the seagods of antiquity. The fisherman also figures several times in representations of the trades. Here De Gheyn releases the subject from its allegorical and historical restraints.

In Bologna, in the 1580s, there existed a strong tendency on the part of artists and writers towards the use of themes from every-day life, as a reaction against the literary bias of the mannerist tradition. Beggars, cripples, vendors, butchers etc. became acceptable subjects on canvas and paper in Annibale's circle.[3] It would be interesting to know to what extent De Gheyn's conception of this drawing stems from this environment.

[1] (1) Net-makers, sitting on the beach, Stockholm, National Museum, Inv. no. Auck 201; monogram and dated 1602. (2) Sale S. Feitama, Amsterdam 16.10.1758, Kbk L no. 26: 'Een strand met vischersschuitjes aan de een zijde, en aan de andere zijde verscheidene vischers, in 1602 met de pen. 7½–12 duim.' Now in Frankfurt a.M., Städelsches Kunstinstitut, inv. no. 801, dated in verso "1602", reproduced in *Stift und Feder*, 1926 no. 35. [2] Apart from the drawing for the engraving of the whale driven ashore at Katwijk, Goltzius depicted several fishermen: Reznicek nos. 52, 55/5 (1606, apostles), 154 (1615, allegory 'Aqua') and 191a (1607, representation of the trades). [3] See: A. W. A. Boschloo, *De nieuwe werkelijkheidsbenadering van Annibale Carracci*, Groningen, 1963 (typewritten manuscript at the Institute for the History of Art, University of Groningen).

28. Jan van Goyen, *Dune landscape with four travellers near a tree* p. 155

DATA: Black chalk, on white paper 176 x 271 mm. Signed in the lower right corner: 'I V GOIEN 162.' (partly cut off). Watermark no. 11.

EXHIBITIONS: The Hague 1902, no. 22; Amsterdam 1903, no. 59; Leiden 1916A, no. 52; Den Haag 1930, I no. 54; Groningen 1931, no. 60; Groningen 1948, no. 95; The Hague 1955, no. 25; Vancouver 1958, no. 30; Leiden/Arnhem 1960, no. 68.

PROVENANCE: Collection Hofstede de Groot, inv. no. 130, bequest 1914, no. 79; — Groninger Museum voor Stad en Lande, inv. no. 1931–159.

When we compare the drawing with some landscapes signed and dated 1627, we are convinced that the date in the lower right corner, which has been partly cut off, must have been the same: Berlin, Kupferstichkabinett, cat. Bock/Rosenberg 1930, nos. 11803 and 2740; Berlin, coll. J. Otto, Herdsmen and cattle in a ferry[1] and Cart and travellers in a dune landscape;[2] Formerly Kassel, coll. Habich, Travellers and cattle on a ferry. See also the text of no. 101.

[1] Exhibited Leiden/Arnhem 1960, no. 67.   [2] Exhibited Leiden/Arnhem 1960, no. 66*.

29. Jan van Goyen, *Anglers on a high bridge*   p. 156

DATA: Black chalk, grey wash, on white paper 113 x 198 mm. Signed in the lower left corner: 'VG 1651'. Verso: owner's mark Von Heyl zu Herrnsheim (Lugt 2879). Watermark no. 12.

LITERATURE: Henkel 1916, p. 341; Van Regteren Altena 1931, p. 73; Van Gelder, no. 34a; Van Regteren Altena 1960, no. 38.

EXHIBITIONS: Leiden 1916A, no. 54; The Hague 1930, I no. 58; Groningen 1931, no. 64; Groningen 1952, no. 35*; The Hague 1955, no. 26; Vancouver 1958, no. 31*; Leiden/Arnhem 1960, no. 88*; Brussels 1961, no. 41; Prague 1966, no 67.

PROVENANCE: Sale Van der Marck, Amsterdam 29.11.1773, no. 232 (L. 2206); Sale Boers, The Hague 21.9.1818, Kbk F, no. 23 (L. 9440); Sale Von Heyl zu Herrnsheim, Stuttgart 25.5.1903, no. 148; — Art dealer Boerner, Leipzig, Lagerliste 1909 no. 72, 1910 no. 61; — Art dealer Strölin, Paris; — Collection Hofstede de Groot, inv. no. 492, bequest 1914, no. 83; — Groninger Museum voor Stad en Lande, inv. no. 1931–163.

Two other drawings,[1] both dated 1651, are very similar to our landscape, to the extent that one would almost think the three drawings had been made on the same midsummer afternoon.[2] In his broadcast lecture for 'Openbaar Kunstbezit',[3] Van Regteren Altena touches upon the connection with Ostade's etching:[4] 'When he [Van Goyen] catches sight of the ramshackle little bridge, he remembers that Ostade etched something like it and he takes his viewing point from the same side; assuming that he did not invent it himself at any rate.' Indeed, Ostade's etching had an enormous influence, as the theme recurs frequently in the years around 1650.[5] A copy after our drawing was sold at auction sale Peltzer.[6]

[1] Coll. Dr W. Beck, Berlin-Friedenau, 112 x 197 mm, signed and dated 1651; Coll. Prof. E. Perman, Stockholm, exh. Laren 1962, no. 46, 114 x 196 mm, signed and dated 1651.   [2] As the three drawings have the same measurements, we are tempted to regard them as leaves from the same sketch-book.   [3] 1962, no. 38.   [4] Bartsch 26.   [5] Other versions of the theme appear in such number that a detailed study is required in order to make a distinction between example and imitation.   [6] Stuttgart 13.5.1914, no. 157*, circular, diameter 20 cm. Another drawing by Van Goyen with a high wooden bridge is in Berlin, Kupferstichkabinett, cat. Bock/Rosenberg 1930, no 11810.

30. Jan van Goyen, *View on a river with a ruined church*   p. 157

DATA: Black chalk, grey and bistre wash, on white paper 189 x 302 mm. Signed in the lower right corner: 'VG 1651'. Verso: 'A. Wangoing'.

LITERATURE: Henkel 1916, p. 341.

EXHIBITIONS: Amsterdam 1903, no. 60; Leiden 1916, no. 53; The Hague 1930, I no. 55; Groningen 1931, no. 61.

26. Jacques de Gheyn II, *A blowing trumpeter*

PROVENANCE: Art dealer Paul Mathey, Paris 1903; — Collection Hofstede de Groot, inv. no. 197, bequest 1914, no. 80; — Groninger Museum voor Stad en Lande, inv. no. 1931–160.

To judge from a number of other dated views of mountainous landscapes,[1] Van Goyen must have travelled in the east of The Netherlands and in Germany in the autumn of the year 1651. This beautiful drawing is also very similar to a signed landscape dated 1652, formerly in the collection of Sir Bruce Ingram.[2]

[1] The Elterberg, sale A. Langen, München 5.6.1899, no. 120. Mountainous river-landscape, coll. C. R. Rudolf, London, 1955, photograph Courtauld Institute, London. Mountainous river-landscape, coll. Ten Cate, Almelo, Exh. Leiden/Arnhem 1960, no. 87 (same measurements as our drawing).   [2] Now in the Fitzwilliam Museum, Cambridge (same measurements as our drawing).

31. Jan van Goyen, *Seashore with boats and carts* p. 158

DATA: Black chalk, grey wash, on white paper 112 x 197 mm. Signed in the lower right corner: 'VG 1653'. Watermark no. 13.
LITERATURE: Henkel 1916, p. 341; Hirschmann, p. 404.
EXHIBITIONS: Leiden 1916 I, no. 56; The Hague 1930, I no. 57; Groningen 1931, no. 63.
PROVENANCE: Sale Warneck, Paris 10.5.1905, no 168. — Collection Hofstede de Groot, inv. no. 342, bequest 1914, no. 82; — Groninger Museum voor Stad en Lande, inv. no. 1931–162.

Many drawings of beach scenes by Van Goyen still survive. His skill in suggesting spatial depth merely by organizing the *staffage* is often surprising. In many cases, the tower of the church at Scheveningen is added, but topographical details are often irrelevant to Van Goyen. There is another beach scene from 1653[1] which has much in common with our drawing. The spatial organization is achieved by a chain of boats, figures and carts from the right foreground to the left background, and the boats show the same sweeping lines. The catalogue of the exhibition at Leiden in 1916 gives the date erroneously as 1650.

[1] Art dealer Parsons, London, magazine catalogue 41 (1923) no 205*.

32. Jan van Goyen?, *Old town on a river* p. 159

DATA: Black chalk, grey wash, on white paper 179 x 276 mm. Signed on the lower left side: 'VG 1653'. Watermark no. 14.
LITERATURE: Henkel 1916, p. 341; Becker, *Neue Folge*, no. 13*; Bernt I, no. 269*.
EXHIBITIONS: Amsterdam 1903, no. 61; Leiden 1916A, no. 55; The Hague 1930, I no. 59; Groningen 1931, no. 65; The Hague 1955, no. 27.
PROVENANCE: Sale V. van Gogh, Amsterdam 2.12.1913, no. 1206; — Collection Hofstede de Groot, inv. no. 541, bequest 1914, no. 84; — Groninger Museum voor Stad en Lande, inv. no. 1931–164.

The drawing shows several weaknesses in execution. It lacks Van Goyen's usual pointedness and there are a few indistinct areas. The tedious hatching of the wall and roof of the large house to the right is something one would not expect from the draughtsman of our Anglers on a high bridge (no. 29).

On the other hand, the composition shows the typical triangular construction that we know so well in Van Goyen's paintings and drawings.[1] Also the motif has often been used, although we do not know of another exactly similar representation. If our drawing is a copy, then certainly it is one after an unknown original.

[1] Painting in the collection Mrs. G. Hart, London, Exh. Leiden/Arnhem 1960, no. 46*, signed and dated 1653. Drawing in the collection De Grez, Brussels, cat. 1913, no. 1412, exh. Rotterdam 1955, no. 44*, Vancouver 1958, no. 33*.

33. Copy after Jan van Goyen, *Landscape with travellers in front of an inn* p. 160

DATA: Black chalk, grey wash, on white paper 180 x 282 mm.
EXHIBITIONS: Leiden 1916A, no. 60; The Hague 1930, I no. 56; Groningen 1931, no. 62.
PROVENANCE: Collection Hofstede de Groot, inv. no. 257, bequest 1914, no. 81; — Groninger Museum voor Stad en Lande, inv. no. 1931–161.

Certainly a copy, probably after an unknown original by Van Goyen of ca. 1650. Although the copyist did not forge Van Goyen's signature or monogram, it was his obvious intent to draw a 'Van Goyen', and not altogether without success, as Hofstede de Groot still believed in its authenticity. Yet there can be no doubt of its being a copy, when we see the house drawn like a profile in a stage set, lacking in depth and sense of construction. It is true that in general the buildings in Van Goyen's paintings and drawings are not the best part, but in this case the weaknesses are such that they do not admit of the attribution to the artist.

34. Copy after Jan van Goyen, *A canal in a town with a watermill and an arched bridge* p. 161

DATA: Black chalk, grey wash, on white paper 117 x 195 mm. Signed in the lower right corner: 'VG 1653'. Watermark no. 15.
LITERATURE: Henkel 1916, p. 341; Hirschmann, p. 404.
EXHIBITIONS: London 1879, no. 465?; The Hague 1902, no. 23; Amsterdam 1903, no. 62; Leiden 1916A, no. 57; The Hague 1930, I no. 53; Groningen 1931, no. 59; Groningen 1952, no. 36.
PROVENANCE: Collection Hofstede de Groot, inv. no. 129, bequest 1914, no. 78; — Groninger Museum voor Stad en Lande, inv. no. 1931–158.

The drawing is connected with an engraving by Jan de Visscher.[1] The quality, however, is not what we expect from a Van Goyen, as there are several weak details to be noticed. The muddled drawing and lack of clarity make it probable that we are dealing with a copy here.

There are four other drawings[2] related to ours by the composition. In all three versions a row of houses, forming the bank of a canal, is depicted to the left. In the middle of the scene, an arched bridge spans the canal; a little further away from the spectator, a church can be seen, also on the left bank. The three other drawings are of a better quality, giving a very clear atmospheric effect. Our drawing, which shows the imprint of the copying needle, was probably executed specially for the purpose of the etching, as the slightly altered composition would have been better suited to the decorative requirements of the engraving.

[¹] Hollstein VIII, p. 163; Le Blanc IV, p. 136, no. 65. One out of a series of twelve landscapes with canals, see fig. 12.   [²] (1) Sale Van Gogh, Amsterdam 2.12.1913, no. 333*, 115 x 195 mm, signed and dated VG 1653. (2) Private collection, Bern; exh. Bremen 1967, no. 170*.   (3) Formerly coll. Basan, Paris; see Weigel 1865, p. 47, no. 72/73 and p. 255, no. 2984. (4) Dresden. Kupferstichkabinett, leaf no. 39 of a sketch-book; see fig. 13. For this information we are indebted to Dr Hans-Ulrich Beck, Munich.

Fig. 12. Jan de Visscher, *A canal in a town with a watermill and an arched bridge.* Engraving after cat. no. 34

Fig. 13. Jan van Goyen, *Landscape with a canal.* Drawing, Dresden, Kupferstichkabinett

35. Jan Hackaert, *Italian landscape after Jan Both*   p. 162

DATA: Pen and bistre, grey wash, on white paper 198 x 298 mm. Signed in the upper left corner: 'JH f 1661'. Verso: the beginning of a sketch.

EXHIBITIONS: Groningen 1915, no. 34; Leiden 1916C, no. 54; The Hague 1930, I no. 60; Groningen 1931, no. 66; The Hague 1955, no. 28.

PROVENANCE: Sale Della Faille Waerloos a.o., Amsterdam 19.1.1904, no. 37; — Collection Hofstede de Groot, inv. no. 246, bequest 1914, no. 37; — Groninger Museum voor Stad en Lande, inv. no. 1931–165.

This landscape shows exactly the same composition as a painting[1] and two other drawings,[2] all attributed to Jan Both. The relation between Hackaert and Both has often been debated. Dr Stelling-Michaud wrote in 1936[3]: '... jedoch scheint es mir wahrscheinlich, dass er [Hackaert] das Atelier des Malers Jan Both besuchte, welcher im Jahre 1640 nach einem vierzigjährigen Aufenthalt in Rom in seine Vaterstadt zurückgekehrt war ... Auch die Zeichnungen der beiden Maler wiesen manchmal solche Ähnlichkeiten auf, dass man sie verwechseln könnte. So ist es anzunehmen, dass Hackaert bei diesem vermutlichen Lehrer sein Handwerk erlernt hat, bevor er Anno 1653, ein Jahr nach dem Tode seines Vaters, nach Italien zog.' In a publication[4] in the following year Dr Stelling-Michaud again touches upon the subject: 'Ihre [Both and Hackaert] Zeichnungen werden oft verwechselt. In der Tat gibt es bei Hackaert zwei sehr verschiedene Weisen, in Tusche mit Feder und Pinsel zu zeichnen. Diejenige, die man die topographische nennen könnte, bei der die Feder ein wenig wie die Nadel des Stechers arbeitet, ist ihm persönlich eigen. Die Blätter des Wiener Atlas Blaeu gehören zu dieser Art. Die andere, die nicht sorgfältig beobachtend, nicht so ausführlich und eingehend und auch nicht so plastisch, aber dafür breiter, luftiger und summarischer in der Strichführung ist, schliesst sich an Jan Boths Technik an' (p. 17) and in a note: '... Es ist sehr gut möglich, dass

Fig. 14. Jan Both, *Italian landscape*. Drawing, Berlin, Kupferstichkabinett

Hackaert, vor seiner Italienreise und vielleicht noch später, Zeichnungen van Jan Both kopiert hat.' W. Bernt, in his entry[5] on Hackaert, poses the same questionmarks: '... Seine Lehrer sind nicht bekannt ... die Möglichkeit der Verwechslung mit J. Both [besteht].'
 Our drawing has the important function of confirming Dr Stelling-Michaud's supposition. Probably Hackaert was in the possession of, or had access to, some of Both's drawings, for the present study, dated 1661 (Both died in 1652), is apparently a close imitation of Both's landscapes.
 If our drawing had not been signed and dated, it would now doubtless bear the name of

52. Frederic de Moucheron, *Mountainous landscape near the Grande Chartreuse, Grenoble*

72

Jan Both, as has happened in other cases. Comparison with our drawing shows that a drawing in London,[6] according to A. M. Hind a preparatory sketch by Both for his etching 'Le grand arbre' (Bartsch 3), may have been executed by Hackaert. The attribution to Both of a drawing in Dyon,[7] probably prompted by its likeness to a painting by Jan Both in the Wallace collection,[8] would also have to be revised.

[1] Hofstede de Groot 1907–28, IX, no. 284; sale Perkins, London 14.6.1890, no. 3; sale Earl of Derby a.o. (anonymous part), London 2.7.1954, no. 75. [2] Berlin, Kupferstichkabinett, cat. Bock-Rosenberg 1930, no. 12241, Tafel 72; signed J. Both, pen and brown ink, washed, 308 x 412 mm; ex coll. Von Beckerath (see fig. 14). The second drawing is in London, The British Museum, cat. A. M. Hind, Vol. III, 1926, p. 48 no. 3 verso. [3] Dr S. Stelling-Michaud, 'Die Via Mala im Jahre 1655 wie sie Jan Hackaert sah und zeichnete', in *Anzeiger für Schweizerische Altertumskunde*, XXXVIII, 1936, Heft 4, p. 261–273. [4] Dr S. Stelling-Michaud, *Unbekannte Schweizer Landschaften aus dem XVII. Jahrhundert, Zeichnungen und Schilderungen von Jan Hackaert und anderen Holländischen Malern*, Zürich/Leipzig, 1937. [5] Bernt, no. 280. [6] The British Museum, cat. A. M. Hind III, 1926, p. 50, no. 11, 251 x 191 mm; there is also a painting by Both, corresponding with this drawing and Both's etching: Hofstede de Groot 1907–28, no. 277B, Puerto Rico, Pounce Museum of Art; repr. in: *Vier generaties Nijstad*, 1962*. [7] Musée de Dijon, ex. coll. His de la Salle (don 1865), cat. no. CA834. [8] Hofstede de Groot 1907–28, IX, no. 123.

36. Nicolaes van Haeften?, *Sheet of studies with twenty-one sketches* p. 163

DATA : Pen and bistre, on white paper 147 x 221 mm. Watermark no. 16.
LITERATURE : Hirschmann, p. 204.
EXHIBITIONS : Groningen 1915, no. 25; Leiden 1916C, no. 46; The Hague 1930, I no. 45; Groningen 1931, no. 51.
PROVENANCE : Sale Van Gogh, Amsterdam 2.12.1913, no. 255; — Collection Hofstede de Groot, inv. no. 543, bequest 1914, no. 28; — Groninger Museum voor Stad en Lande, inv. no. 1931–150.

It is not likely that, as tradition would have it, Gerbrand van den Eeckhout made the present study. Not only is the quality far below that of Eeckhout, but also the type of figures originates from another mould. There is a vague connection with the technique of Philips Koninck's figure-drawings, but probably the sheet does not even originate from the school of Rembrandt. It may have been the work of a rather late genre painter[1] copying an example of ca. 1660, as indeed Nicolaes van Haeften must have done, to judge from his paintings[2] in which we can see the same type of figures.

[1] Prof. Van Regteren Altena suggested that the study might be by the hand of Nicolaes van Haeften. [2] Photographs of a number of his paintings are present in the collections of the Rijksbureau voor Kunsthistorische Documentatie, The Hague.

37. Hendrik Johan Haverman, *Portrait of the painter Jacob Maris* p. 164

DATA : Black chalk, on white paper 300 x 272 mm. Recto, pen and brown ink, upper right corner: 'H. J. Haverman '97'.
LITERATURE : Van Regteren Altena 1931, p. 70.
EXHIBITIONS : Groningen 1915, no. 33; The Hague 1930, I no. 61; Groningen 1931, no. 67.
PROVENANCE : Coll. Paul Durieu; — Collection M. Nijhoff, The Hague; — Collection Hof-

stede de Groot, inv. no. 72, bequest 1914, no. 36; — Groninger Museum voor Stad en Lande, inv. no. 1931–166.

Hofstede de Groot had four portraits by Haverman in his possession, representing Bredius, Toorop, Deyserinck and Maris. This was the only modern drawing in the collection bequeathed to Groningen. Dr Marius, in her survey of nineteenth century-painting in Holland, mentions[1] that in 1897 Haverman started to draw portraits of famous contemporaries for the newly founded periodical *Woord en Beeld*. A xylograph after another drawing by Haverman, however, also representing a portrait of Maris, was published[2] instead of our portrait. It is more likely that our drawing was made as a preparatory sketch for a painted portrait[3] that is similar in details and composition. A third drawing, also a portrait by Haverman of the painter Jacob Maris, in the same technique as the one in Groningen, is preserved in Rotterdam.[4]

[1] G. H. Marius, *De Hollandsche schilderkunst in de negentiende eeuw*, 's-Gravenhage, 1903, p. 458. [2] *Woord en Beeld*, II, 1897, p. 214. [3] Exposition The Hague 1903, no. 17; Sale Bosman, The Hague 6.5.1908, no. 43*; present whereabouts unknown. At the sale of Haverman's atelier in The Hague 13.5.1930, there were two painted portraits of Jacob Maris (nos. 83 and 84). [4] Museum Boymans-van Beuningen; dated 1898, reproduced in *Onze Kunst* I, 1902, opposite p. 12 as an illustration to a study on Jacob Maris by Jan Veth.

38, 39. Guilliam de Heer, *Wedding-portraits of Johannes Bogaert and Maria Wijnands* p. 166, 167

DATA: Pen and black ink, on vellum 248 x 184 mm. Signed on the lower left side: 'G de Heer'. Inscribed on the upper left side: 'Aetatis Suae 31, A°. 1634' and 'Aetatis Suae 33, 1634'.

LITERATURE: Henkel 1916, p. 343; Hirschmann, p. 407.

EXHIBITIONS: Leiden 1916A, nos. 61 and 62; The Hague 1930, I nos. 62, 63, and 64; Groningen 1931, nos. 68 and 69; Groningen 1952, nos 48 and 49.

PROVENANCE: Sale Van der Willigen, Den Haag 10.6.1874, no. 117 (L. 34966). Sale Mrs. E. Brightwen, London 19.6.1906, no. 156; — Sale Duval, Amsterdam 21.6.1910, no. 164*; — Sale F. A. v. S., Amsterdam 11.6.1912, no. 441; — Collection Hofstede de Groot, inv. nos. 493 and 494, bequest 1914, nos. 38 and 39; — Groninger Museum voor Stad en Lande, inv. no. 1931–167 and 1931–168.

These stately portraits have been executed without the usual profusion of accessories that in most cases decorate the portraits of Guilliam de Heer. Almost always a number of other people and a dense undergrowth are depicted. Yet the few elements that have been represented here, appearing as incidental decoration, reveal the nature and identity of the portraits. To the left of the woman, a thistle and a strand of ivy can be seen. The latter is entwining a treetrunk. Both are symbols for conjugal faith and love.[1] The couple is standing in an idyllic landscape, with sheds and a small rowing-boat in the distance. The park-like aspect of the landscape, in combination with the ivy and thistle, could also be an allusion to the Gardens of Love, in which Rubens and Frans Hals depicted their marriage-portraits.[2]

We may safely assume that the present drawings are meant as a wedding portrait. The marriage evidently took place in Haarlem[3] in the year 1634, according to the inscriptions. The man was born in 1603 and the woman in 1601. The parrot sitting on the tree-trunk and the snail in front of the woman tell us her name. In the *Defensorium immaculatae Virginitatis*[4] by Franciscus de Retza (†1425) the parrot and the snail are mentioned as symbols of the Virgin Mary.

In the municipal archives of Haarlem[5] there is only one couple mentioned that satisfies the following requirements: married in 1634, of a more or less distinguished family, the first name of the woman Maria, the man born in the year 1603. A Johannes Bogaert married Maria Wijnands on June 25th, 1634. Bogaert was born in 1603; it is not possible to check the year in which the woman was born, as her entry in the marriage records only reports the attestation of Heemstede, a small village in the neighbourhood of Haarlem. The father of the man, also called Johannes, was a protestant clergyman, whose portrait was painted by Frans Hals.[6] Jan van de Velde engraved two portraits (Franken en Van der Kellen, nos. 4 and 5) of him.

[1] A thorough analysis of the two symbols is given by E. de Jongh and P. J. Vinken, 'Frans Hals als voortzetter van een emblematische traditie' in *Oud Holland* LXXVI, 1961, no. 3, p. 117–152. The article mainly deals with Hals' marriage-portraits of 1622 of Isaac Massa and Beatrix van der Laan in the Amsterdam Rijksmuseum. As De Heer, however, worked in Haarlem during the time that this portrait could be seen there, we may assume that he knew the emblematic content of the portraits. [2] See the same article, p. 138–139: the boat is also used as a symbol of marriage in Dürer's engraving of a couple on horseback, and in an engraving after A. van der Venne, illustration to Jacob Cats' *Houwelick*, etc., Middelburg, 1625 (reproduced p. 134), and in a nuptial medal by Wouter Muller, verso (reproduced p. 136). [3] There is not much known about the course of Guilliam de Heer's life. As these portraits, however, are typical of the style in which the Haarlem portraitists worked, we may assume that De Heer's patrons in this case were inhabitants of that city. [4] 'Psiticus a natura ave si dicere valet, quare virgo pura per ave non generaret?' and 'Si concha rore desuper prolis fecundare claret, cur rorante pneumate virgo non generaret?' Quotation taken from Timmers; see Bibliography Timmers, no. 1138. See also: E. K. J. Reznicek, 'De reconstructie van "t'Altaer van S. Lucas" van Maerten van Heemskerck', in *Oud Holland* LXX, 1955, p. 233–245. [5] We owe much to the kind cooperation of the Archivist of Haarlem, Dr G. H. Kurtz. [6] Now lost; see W. R. Valentiner, *Frans Hals* (Klassiker der Kunst), Stuttgart/Berlin, 1921, no. 5; Hofstede de Groot 1907–28, III, no. 159.

40. Jacob Koninck?, *Farmhouse by the waterside*   p. 165

DATA: Pen and bistre, white body-colour, on white paper 180 x 230 mm. Verso, in sanguine: 'p ko', in pen and brown ink: 'p ko', owner's mark Sträter (Lugt 787).

LITERATURE: Becker, no. 21*; Gerson 1936, no. Z31 and p. 62*.

EXHIBITIONS: The Hague 1902, no. 26; Leiden 1916C, no. 57; The Hague 1930, I no. 67; Groningen 1931, no. 70; Groningen 1952, no. 54.

PROVENANCE: Sale Vis Blockhuizen, Rotterdam 23.10.1871, no. 328 (L. 32660); — Sale Sträter, Stuttgart 10.5.1898, no. 1141 (L. 56298); Art dealer Gutekunst, Bern; — Art dealer Colnaghi, London 1902; — Collection Hofstede de Groot, inv. no. 182, bequest 1914, no. 16; — Groninger Museum voor Stad en Lande, inv. no. 1931–169.

Gerson attributed[1] this drawing to Philips Koninck, probably because of what seems to be a signature in verso: 'p ko'. A drawing in Weimar by Bartholomeus Breenbergh,[2] inscribed in verso 'P. koning 1669' is attributed to Philips Koninck on the same grounds, although F. Lugt suggested that these inscriptions could have been a collection-mark of Philips Koninck. Our drawing is undoubtedly by the same hand as two landscapes in Paris.[3] It is also very similar to a drawing in London[4] inscribed in verso by a contemporary hand: ' I Cooning'. Three landscapes in Rotterdam[5] inscribed in verso in a contemporary hand 'J. Kooninck', and a drawing in Amsterdam[6] attributed by Henkel and Schneider to Jacob, also make the present attribution plausible.

[¹] Gerson 1936, no. Z31* and p. 62.   [²] Gerson 1936, no. Z80* and p. 66.   [³] (1) Louvre, Lugt 1929–33, III, no. 1346*, as Jacob Koninck; Hofstede de Groot 1906, no. 664 as Rembrandt; Gerson 1936, no. Z74 as Philips Koninck, with reference to our 'signed' drawing; a copy is in the collection of F. Lugt, inv. no. 3750, formerly in the Albertina, Vienna. (2) Louvre, Lugt, 1929–33, III, no. 1345*, as Jacob Koninck; a copy was at the auction sale M. van Gogh, Amsterdam 16.7.1930, no. 97* as Jacob Koninck.   [⁴] British Museum, inv. no. 1912–12–14–17, cat. A. M. Hind. I, 1915, p. 81, no. 2, Pl. XLVII.   [⁵] Museum Boymans-van Beuningen, inv. nos. JK1–3.   [⁶] Rijksprentenkabinet, inv. no. A4291, Henkel 1942, no. 1; Schneider (see Bibliography) no. Z IV.

41. Philips Koninck, *View over a wide landscape near Haarlem*   p. 168

DATA: Pen and bistre, bistre wash, on brownish paper 140 x 220 mm, pasted on paper. Recto, lower left corner: removed inscription 'Rembrandt'.

LITERATURE: Hirschmann, p. 202*; Becker, no. 23*; Gerson 1936, no. Z30 and p. 59*; Van Gelder 1959, no. 97a*; Frerichs 1959, no. 33*.

EXHIBITIONS: The Hague 1902, no. 45; Leiden 1903, no. 12; Paris 1908, no. 475; Leiden 1916C, no. 61; The Hague 1930, I no. 65; Groningen 1931, no. 71; Groningen 1948, no. 96; Groningen 1952, no. 53*; The Hague 1955, no. 31; Leiden 1956, no. 144; Vancouver 1958, no. 42*.

PROVENANCE: Collection Dimsdale; Art dealer T. Humphrey Ward, London 1906; — Collection Hofstede de Groot, inv. no. 310, bequest 1914, no. 17; — Groninger Museum voor Stad en Lande, inv. no. 1931–170.

Miss Frerichs¹ explained the empty area in the foreground and the unusual application of perspective of this drawing by suggesting that the draughtsman must have been standing on a tower or the roof of a house. A drawing by Allaert van Everdingen,² showing exactly the same panoramic landscape, but seen from a high dune or a hill with trees to the right, demonstrates that the gist of Miss Frerichs's supposition was correct. It has not been previously

Fig. 15. Philips Koninck, *Landscape with trees on a dune*. Painting, coll. of the late Dr. A. F. Philips, Eindhoven

realized that our drawing has several similarities to a painting by Philips Koninck.[3] Like in the drawing by Van Everdingen, the right foreground of the painting is occupied by a hill with trees to the right; for the rest the painting shows the same bird's eye view as the wide landscape in the two drawings. Since Van Everdingen's landscape makes us fully realize the situation we are tempted to believe that the painting is based on the present drawing, which may be a study after nature. For an analysis of the spiritual contents of the drawing and its relationship with the landscapes of Rembrandt, we have pleasure in referring to the profound treatment by Miss Frerichs.

[1] Broadcast lecture for 'Openbaar Kunstbezit' 1959, no. 33. [2] Leiden, Printroom of the University, inv. no. AW649. [3] Collection of the late Dr A. F. Philips, Eindhoven; Gerson 1936, no. 21. See fig. no. 15.

42. Philips Koninck, *Head of a peasant* p. 169

DATA: Pen and bistre, on light brown paper 65 x 72 mm. Recto, lower left side: 'Brawer'. Verso: 'A. Ostade'.

LITERATURE: Becker, *Neue Folge*, no. 3*.

EXHIBITIONS: Leiden 1916A, no. 20; The Hague 1930, I no. 35; Groningen 1931, no. 41; Groningen 1948, no. 90; Groningen 1952, no. 19.

PROVENANCE: Sale Warneck, Paris 10.5.1905, no. 235; — Collection Hofstede de Groot, inv. no. 267, bequest 1914, no. 15; — Groninger Museum voor Stad en Lande, inv. no. 1931–140.

This small study belongs to a series of about twelve drawings of burlesque subjects, seven of which are now in the National Museum of Stockholm. The head in our drawing appears in

Fig. 16. Philips Koninck, *Peasants at backgammon*. Drawing, formerly coll. Fairfax-Murray

another sketch, attributed to Philips Koninck.[1] As the traditional attribution to Adriaan Brouwer is not supported by any evidence,[2] our drawing is provisionally credited here to Koninck, pending further research on the subject.

[1] Gerson 1936, no. Z246; Coll. Fairfax Murray, London; sale De Robiano, Amsterdam 15.6.1926, no. 391*. See fig. 16. [2] The group of drawings in Stockhlom was rejected as Brouwer by G. Knuttel. See: G. Knuttel, *Adriaan Brouwer, the master and his work,* The Hague, 1962, p. 172.

Fig. 17. Philips Koninck, *Derision of Christ.* Drawing, formerly art-dealer Artaria, Vienna

43. Philips Koninck, *Study of three heads* p. 170

DATA: Pen and bistre, on white paper 110 x 149 mm.

LITERATURE: Hirschmann, p. 408*; Becker, *Neue Folge,* no. 4*; Gerson 1936, no. Z257 and p. 68, 69 and 77.

EXHIBITIONS: Leiden 1916A, no. 21; The Hague 1930, I no. 34; Groningen 1931, no. 40; Groningen 1948, no. 89; The Hague 1955, no. 30.

PROVENANCE: Sale M. Strauss, Wien 2.5.1906, no. 14; — Collection Hofstede de Groot, inv. no. 266, bequest 1914, no. 18; — Groninger Museum voor Stad en Lande, inv. no. 1931–139.

Hofstede de Groot bought this drawing as being an Adriaan Brouwer. Gerson[1] was the first to attribute it to Philips Koninck: 'Von Brouwers genialem Strich findet sich hier doch keine Spur.' We believe that the figure in profile to the left was in Koninck's mind when he drew a Derision of Christ,[2] in which it appears in the same position.

[1] Gerson 1936, no. Z257. [2] Gerson 1936, no. A183, sale Boreel a.o., Amsterdam 15.6.1908, no. 496. See fig. 17.

44. Philips Koninck?, *Farmhouse in a hilly landscape* p. 171

DATA: Pen and bistre, grey and bistre wash, on white paper 164 x 309 mm. Verso, in a quasi-old hand: 'P. de Koning fecit' and 'k'–'.

LITERATURE: Hirschmann, p. 202; Gerson 1936, no. XXIX and p. 59.

EXHIBITIONS: Leiden 1916C, no. 59; The Hague 1930, I no. 66; Groningen 1931, no. 72; The Hague 1955, no. 29.

PROVENANCE: Art dealer Colnaghi, London 1912; — Collection Hofstede de Groot, inv. no. 487, bequest 1914, no. 18; — Groninger Museum voor Stad en Lande, inv. no. 1931–171.

Among the many landscape drawings of Rembrandt and his school, there is a large number which show the same stylistic characteristics as we find in the present drawing. The most striking of these characteristics are the long attenuated lines, interrupted by small zigzag lines, and the manner in which the foliage is drawn. Between 1640 and 1642 Rembrandt drew a number of similar landscapes[1] in which the vegetation seems to have been infected by a strange virus, disturbing and accelerating the normal growth, so that the foliage looks like cabbage leaves. Philips and Jacob Koninck, Abraham Furnerius, Anthonie van Borssum, Lambert Doomer, Johannes Ruisscher and Jacob Esselens occasionally made use of this manner in their own way.

Probably the rather poor quality was Gerson's[2] reason for rejecting our drawing as not being by Philips Koninck, but closer to Koninck's brother-in-law Furnerius. The possibility of Koninck's authorship, however, remains to be considered. Prof. Van Regteren Altena has drawn our attention to the resemblance of a signed landscape by Koninck in the collection of F. Lugt (Gerson 1936, no. 62, Pl. 26). When Koninck came to Amsterdam, in 1640–41, he could have come under the influence of Rembrandt's drawings of 1640–42, mentioned above. Later on, after this Rembrandtesque interlude, Philips could have developed an elaborate manner, one more his own.

Neither can we discard the possibility of Furnerius' authorship. Notwithstanding the general agreement existing about the Furnerius group, there is no decisive proof that what we call 'Furnerius' does in fact deserve that name. A corpus of ca. one hundred drawings has been built up on account of a probably eighteenth century annotation[3] occuring on a number of drawings[4] in various collections. Our drawing has its equivalent among several drawings of this Furnerius group, in which fertile country with luxuriant vegetation and ripening corn-fields are depicted.[5]

The compositions of Koninck and Furnerius all show a specific method of dealing with the problem of how to lead the eye from our reality into the imaginary distance of the picture. Seghers' conception of spatial organization had made artists aware of the idea that we can enter the space of a painting or drawing in surprisingly new ways. Because of the generally applied solutions to this spatial problem, we are not able to draw any conclusion from the compositional particularities of our drawing. Notwithstanding the wealth of comparative material, we are forced to suspend a final judgment concerning the artist's identity. As the inscriptions in verso indicate a tradition that leads back to Koninck, the drawing is here provisionally credited to Philips Koninck.

[1] Benesch IV, nos. 496–498, figs. 617, 619, 621.　[2] See Bibliography Gerson 1936.　[3] See K. T. Parker, *Catalogue of the drawings of the Ashmolean Museum,* Oxford, I, 1938, no. 132.　[4] Leningrad, Hermitage, Landscape with a bridge.

Inv. no 3075, reproduced in Colin T. Eisler, *Flemish and Dutch drawings from the 15th to the 18th century*, London, 1964, Pl. 97. Two landscape-drawings in Dresden, one of which is reproduced in Henkel 1931, Pl. LXVIII; of the other drawing there is a photograph in the Rijksbureau voor Kunsthistorische Documentatie, The Hague. Oxford, Ashmolean Museum, K. T. Parker, *Catalogue* etc. I, 1938, no. 132. Cambridge, Fitzwilliam Museum, inv. no. PD 340-1963, ex coll. Sir Bruce Ingram; see exh. cat. *'Rembrandt and his circle'*, Fitzwilliam Museum, 1966, no. 30. [5] A.o. Dresden, Kupferstichkabinett, Landscape with cornfields and a village (Photograph in the Rijksbureau voor Kunsthistorische Documentatie, The Hague; in verso inscribed in old German lettering: 'abrahā fournerius'. Stockholm, National Museum, Landscape with trees to the left and a country road through the cornfields, cat. Kruse VII, 1920, no. 4.

45. Jan Lievens, *Portrait of William Kerr, third Earl of Lothian*   p. 172

DATA: Black chalk, on white paper 205 x 210 mm. Signed to the left: 'I L'. Recto, lower left corner: owner's mark Gigoux (Lugt 1164). Watermark no. 17.

LITERATURE: Hirschmann, p. 201; Schneider no. Z94.

EXHIBITIONS: The Hague 1902, no. 27; Leiden 1903, no. 77; Groningen 1915, no. 35; Leiden 1916C, no. 70; The Hague 1930, I no. 68; Groningen 1931, no. 73; Groningen 1952, no. 56; Washington 1958-59, no. 74.

PROVENANCE: Sale Gigoux, Paris 20.3.1882, no. 364 (L. 41800); — Art dealer Van Gogh, Amsterdam 1901; — Collection Hofstede de Groot, inv. no. 70, bequest 1914, no. 40; — Groninger Museum voor Stad en Lande, inv. no. 1931-172.

The portrait was formerly regarded as that of the Elector of Brandenburg (see cat. Washington 1958-59). Schneider (see Bibliography) already rejected this identification, preferring to leave the matter undecided.

In the collection of the Marquess of Lothian[1] there is a painted portrait[2] by David Scougall, representing William Kerr, third Earl of Lothian (1605-75). This portrait is a typical example of Scougall's habit of stealing designs from the work of other artists, e.g. he has taken the background and harness from the Van Dyck portrait of James Hamilton, third Marquess and first Duke of Hamilton, now in the collection of the Duke of Hamilton, Hamilton Palace;[3] it seems extremely probable that he has based his drawing of the head, if not on the present drawing, almost certainly on something derived from it.[4] The possibility that the sitter of our portrait is indeed William Kerr is acceptable not only because of the physiological similarity. William's father, Sir Robert Kerr, first Earl of Ancrum, had a portrait made by Jan Lievens during his exile in Amsterdam. In 1654, the year of his death, Ancrum writes to his son: 'thogh I be, by God his mercy, alyve and in health, yet I grow very old, which fhoweth more in one year now then in thrie before, as yow will fee by the difference of my pictures, wherof I haue fent yow one, and hath another much older donne fince, by a good maifter, to beftow upon yow iff I haue my toung to my end, otherwayes yow may call for it at this toun near the new markett, out of the hands of one Mr. Levinus, the Duke of Brandeburg's paynter. He duelt at the figne of the *fleur-de-luce,* and yow may be fure of a good one. He is the better becaufe he hath fo high a conceitt of himfelf that he thinks there is no one to be compaired with him in all Germany, Holland, nor the reft of the 17 Provinces.'[5]

We have no precise data available as to the year in which our portrait was done. Before Lievens established himself in Antwerp in the year 1635, he had been in England, according to Orlers.[6] Whether this journey, for which precise and convincing data are still lacking, actually took place, or not, Lievens could not have executed the drawing on that occasion. The portrait shows a weariness that is unexpected in a man of thirty. William Kerr visited the Netherlands several times: in 1629–30 he 'was present at the capitulation of Bois-le-Duc to the prince of Orange'.[7] In 1650 he 'was a member to the second commission appointed by the estates to proceed on 9 March 1650 to treat with the King at Breda'.[8] On this occasion Lothian also visited other parts of the Netherlands.[9] This may have been the opportunity for having the portrait drawn, though there is no mention of it in the correspondence. Also Ancrum more or less implies in his letter of 1654 that Lievens' name is new to his son. The possibility remains that Lothian went to Amsterdam in 1655, when 'the dead body [of Ancrum] was arrested in May 1655 by his creditors to secure payment of his debts'.[10]

Fig. 18. David Scougall, *Portrait of William Kerr, third Earl of Lothian.*
Painting, Newbattle Abbey near Edinburgh

[1] Newbattle Abbey, near Edinburgh. The collection, other than family portraits, was started by the third Earl of Lothian, who bought from France and the Low Countries.   [2] Canvas, 86 x 51 in., exh. Edinburgh 1884, no. 153. Mentioned in the *Catalogue of original pictures in the house of Newbattle,* a manuscript in the collection of family papers of ca. 1720. See fig. 18.   [3] For the identification we are greatly indebted to Mr. Basil C. Skinner of the Scottish National Portrait Gallery, Edinburgh.   [4] A pedigree of our drawing could not be established because of the countless portraits of anonymous men by Lievens, occurring in old catalogues of auction sales. [5] *Correspondence of Sir Robert Kerr, first Earl of Ancrum and his son William, third Earl of Lothian, 1616–1667,* Vol. II, edited by David Laing, Edinburgh, 1875.   [6] J. Orlers, *Beschrijving der Stadt Leyden,* 1641, p. 377.   [7] *Dictionary of National Biography* Vol. XXXI, p. 64.   [8] Ibidem p. 65.   [9] '... hearing that your Lordship was to be this night at Leyden ...' George Wynrame of Libberton to the Earl of Lothian, May 31, 1650, in *Correspondence,* etc., Vol. II, p. 267. [10] *Dictionary of National Biography* Vol. XXXI, p. 56.

46. Jan Lievens, *Portrait of René Descartes*

p. 173

DATA: Black chalk, on white paper 241 x 206 mm. Verso, in an old hand: 'Renatus Descartes', owner's mark Von Lanna (Lugt 2773). Watermark no. 18.

LITERATURE: Hirschmann, p. 201*; Becker, no. 25*; Schneider, no. z56; Nordström, p. 245, note 92; Lot, p. 8,9*.

EXHIBITIONS: Leiden 1916C, no. 69; The Hague 1930, no. 71; Groningen 1931, no. 74; Groningen 1952, no. 57*; Leiden 1956, no. 152; Ingelheim 1964, no. 47*; London 1964, no. 105; Prague 1966, no. 97*.

PROVENANCE: Sale De Visser, Amsterdam 16.5.1881, no. 488 (L. 41110); — Sale Von Lanna, Stuttgart 6.5.1910, no. 579; — Collection Hofstede de Groot, inv. no. 448, bequest 1914, no. 43; — Groninger Museum voor Stad en Lande, inv. no. 1931–173.

In the De Visser and Von Lanna sales, the portrait was sold as a drawing by Cornelis de Visscher. The present attribution originates from Hofstede de Groot. The sitter can be identified without hesitation as René Descartes. Frans Hals' portrait of the famous French philosopher, painted ca. 1648–49, is preserved in the Louvre. It is known that Rembrandt also made a portrait of Cartesius.[1] Lievens settled in Amsterdam in 1644 and Descartes left Holland for Sweden in 1649. The portrait could have been executed during this period of five years; Schneider reports (p. 7) that particularly in these years Lievens made a great number of portraits of poets, scientists and members of the Dutch aristocracy. The style and costume of our portrait are not at variance with this date.

[1] See handwritten catalogue of the Valerius Röver collection, Library of the Municipal University, Amsterdam; brush drawing; present whereabouts unknown.

47. Jan Lievens, *View on a town, to the left a high tree*

p. 174

DATA: Pen and bistre, on white paper 345 x 328 mm. Watermark no. 19.

LITERATURE: Eisenmann, no. 20; Hirschmann, p. 200; Becker, no. 26; Schneider, no. z168.

EXHIBITIONS: Leiden 1903, no. 78; Leiden 1916C, no. 64; The Hague 1930, I no. 69; Groningen 1931, no. 75; Groningen 1948, no. 97; The Hague 1955, no. 32.

Fig. 19. Jan Lievens, *Town with a windmill.* Drawing, New York, Piermont Morgan Library

PROVENANCE: Sale J. H. Cremer, Amsterdam 15.6.1886, no. 195 (L. 45864); — Sale E. Habich, Stuttgart 27.4.1899, no. 422 (L. 57164); — Art dealer Colnaghi, London 1903; — Collection Hofstede de Groot, inv. no. 199, bequest 1914, no. 41; — Groninger Museum voor Stad en Lande, inv. no. 1931–174.

The composition is based on the principles that Hercules Seghers often used in his landscapes. We cannot enter this town because Lievens conceals the entrance from our view. In doing so the artist obtains a different sense of reality. It almost seems as if these artists were trying to prove the one-sidedness of Van Manders directives for landscape-painting, as expressed in

Fig. 20. Jan Lievens, *The roller-bridge to the Sloterpolder near Amsterdam*.
Drawing, Leiden, Printroom of the University

his *Grondt der Edel vry Schilderconst*. The solution to the problem of the foreground and the continuation of the various planes, as applied in Seghers's work and in the present drawing is at variance with Van Mander's advice in vs. 20 and 22 of the eighth chapter of the '*Leerdicht*'.

Possibly the same town is represented in a drawing by Lievens in New York.[1] The mill and turret, occuring on both drawings, would belong to the towns under the authority of the Elector of Brandenburg, in whose service Lievens was in the year 1654. There is a view of the town of Kleve[2] that is very similar to the present drawing.

[1] Pierpont Morgan Library, inv. no. III 186; Schneider, no. 3, p. 247. See fig. 19. [2] Amsterdam, Rijksprentenkabinet, cat. Henkel, 1942, no. 9, inv. no. A482; Schneider, no. Z142; Henkel 1931, p. 131, exh. Krefeld 1938, no. 89; Düsseldorf 1953, no. 69; Köln 1960–61, no. 78.

48. Copy after Jan Lievens, *The roller-bridge to the Sloterpolder near Amsterdam* p. 175

DATA: Pen and bistre, bistre wash, on brownish paper 174 x 303 mm.
LITERATURE: Hirschmann, p. 199; De Gelder, p. 30, no. 78; Schneider, nos. Z216 and Z216a.
EXHIBITIONS: Amsterdam 1906, no. 147; Groningen 1915, no. 36; Leiden 1916C, no. 65; The Hague 1930, I no. 70; Groningen 1931, no. 76.

PROVENANCE: Sale Van den Berch van Heemstede, Amsterdam 5.6.1905, no. 1249; — Art dealer Fred. Muller, Amsterdam 1906; — Collection Hofstede de Groot, inv. no. 312, bequest 1914, no. 42; — Groninger Museum voor Stad en Lande, inv. no. 1931–175.

Two other versions of the present drawing are known. The original, according to Schneider, passed through the Goldschmidt sale.[1] Another copy is in Leiden.[2] At several old auction sales[3] the drawings are mentioned; it is, however, not possible to judge which of the different versions is meant. See also the text of entry no. 69.

[1] Sale Goldschmidt, Frankfurt am Main, 4.10.1917, no. 340, 130 x 230 mm, ex coll. De Vos and Franck, with repr., to Cassirer; Schneider no. z216; on Japanese paper. [2] Printroom of the University, inv. no. 1624, 207 x 319 mm, also mentioned with Schneider no. z216; De Gelder, no. 78; C. G. 't Hoofd, *24 Gezichten in oud-Amsterdam*, 1925, no. 13; sale Cremer, Amsterdam 15.6.1886, no. 196; sale Piek, Amsterdam 1.6.1897, no. 159; See fig. 20. [3] Sale N. van Bremen, Amsterdam 15.12.1766, no. 753; sale H. Busserus, Amsterdam 21.8.1782, no. 1192; sale G. van Nijmegen, Amsterdam 20.3.1809, no. 34.

49. Copy after Jan Lievens, *View of a small bridge and a farm-house surrounded by trees* p. 176

DATA: Pen and bistre, bistre wash, on brownish Japanese paper 225 x 345 mm. Signed on the lower left side: 'J L fec.' Verso: owner's mark K. E. von Liphart (Lugt 1687), owner's mark R. von Liphart (Lugt 1758) and '1201'.

LITERATURE: Hirschmann, p. 200; Schneider, p. 22 (see no. z218).

EXHIBITIONS: Groningen 1915, no. 38; Leiden 1916c, no. 66; The Hague 1930, I no. 73; Groningen 1931, no. 78; Groningen 1948, no. 98; The Hague 1955, no. 33.

PROVENANCE: Collection K. E. van Liphart; — Sale R. von Liphart, Leipzig 26.4.1898, no. 565 (L. 56238); — Sale O. von Zur Mühlen, Berlin 5.6.1912, no. 312; — Coll. G. von Mallmann, 1912; — Collection Hofstede de Groot, inv. no. 497, bequest 1914, no. 45; — Groninger Museum voor Stad en Lande, inv. no. 1931–177.

Fig. 21. Jan Lievens, *View on a small bridge and a farm-house surrounded by trees.*
Drawing, Paris, coll. F. Lugt

The original version is in the collection of Frits Lugt in Paris (See fig. 21). We do not think that our drawing has been executed by Lievens himself but it may well be contemporary. A drawing, formerly in Vienna,[1] was done by the same hand that made our copy. We are reminded of Eeckhout's drawings of ca. 1670,[2] when his work showed marked similarity to the drawings of Jacob Esselens.

[1] Probably also a copy after a drawing by Lievens, although we have not found the original; Albertina, inv. no. 828–930; Schneider no. Z347; sale Amsterdam 9.12.1930, no. 248; now in coll. Bernard Houthakker, exh. Amsterdam 1964, no. 53. See fig. 22. [2] Collection Sir Bruce Ingram, exh. Rotterdam 1961, no. 35. Amsterdam, Rijksprentenkabinet, inv. nos. A3691, A313 and A4308, Henkel 1942, nos. 12, 21, 13.

Fig. 22. Copy after Jan Lievens, *Landscape with a small village.* Drawing, Amsterdam, coll. Bernhard Houthakker

50. Nicolaas Maes?, *Two studies of Titus van Rijn, Rembrandt's son*   p. 177

DATA: Pen and bistre, bistre wash, on white paper 95 x 112 mm. Watermark no. 20.
LITERATURE: Teding van Berkhout, no. 15; Von Seidlitz, p. 254, no. L57.
EXHIBITIONS: Amsterdam 1913, no. 42; Groningen 1915, no. 52; Leiden 1916B, no. 57; The Hague 1930, I no. 86; Groningen 1931, no. 91; The Hague 1955, no. 44.
PROVENANCE: Art dealer Bourgeois, Paris, 1911; — Collection Hofstede de Groot, inv. no. 462, bequest 1914, no. 94; — Groninger Museum voor Stad en Lande, inv. no. 1931–190.

The core of the work of Rembrandt's pupils in general has been insufficiently published and thus it is very difficult to be definitive in the matter of authenticity. If we work from the few documented drawings by Nicolaes Maes, little can be deduced concerning the present study. W. R. Valentiner (see Bibliography Valentiner 1924) and M. D. Henkel (see Bibliography Henkel 1942), however, attributed a large number of drawings from the Rembrandt school to Nicolaes Maes, and gradually there came into existence a generally accepted corpus of Maes drawings. Compared stylistically with some of the drawings[1] from this corpus, the present study seems to belong to this group. The subject of the drawing also favours this supposition, as scenes with an emphasis on quiet, homely complacency frequently occur in Maes' œuvre. The boy, who is undoubtedly Rembrandt's son Titus, is here in his early' teens. As the drawing seems to have been executed as a quick sketch *a vista* the boy's age may serve to date the drawing at ca. 1653. This is the last year that Maes worked in Rembrandt's atelier, so that a real possibility supports our stylistic attribution.

[¹] Two drawings in Rotterdam, Museum Boymans-van Beuningen, ex. coll. Koenigs and Dalhousie. Inv. no. R64 recto (photograph Gernsheim no. 36643, Valentiner 1924, p. 50, fig. 57) and R119 (photograph Gernsheim no. 36640). A drawing in coll. Strölin, Lausanne, ex-coll. Dalhousie, Valentiner 1924, p. 63, fig. 70.

51. Pieter Molijn, *Winter landscape*   p. 178

DATA : Black chalk, grey wash, on white paper 160 x 261 mm. Watermark no. 21.
LITERATURE : Henkel 1916, p. 342; Hirschmann, p. 404.
EXHIBITIONS : Leiden 1916A, no. 65; The Hague 1930, I no. 74; Groningen 1931, no. 79; The Hague 1955, no. 34; Brussels 1961, no. 32;
PROVENANCE : Sale Roupell, London 12.7.1887, no. 1016 or 1017 (L. 46748); Art dealer Colnaghi, London 1903; — Collection Hofstede de Groot, inv. no. 196, bequest 1914, no. 46; — Groninger Museum voor Stad en Lande, inv. no. 1931–178.

This is probably one item out of a series of the twelve months of the year or the four seasons. In the British Museum¹ there is a winter scene with exactly the same composition, differing only in some of the details. Our drawing probably originates from the same time as the twelve months series in Haarlem,² e.g. 1658. A further indication that this date is probably correct is a drawing in Rotterdam,³ dated 1656, which also closely resembles our drawing.

[¹] Salting collection, inv. no. 1910–2–12–157, 145 x 193 mm, signed. [²] Teylers Museum, inv. nos. 060–71, signed and dated 1658. [³] Museum Boymans-van Beuningen, inv. no. H168; the same measurements as our drawing, 162 x 260 mm; also a winter landscape.

52. Frederic de Moucheron, *Mountainous landscape near the Grande Chartreuse, Grenoble*   p. 72

DATA : Pen and bistre, grey wash, white body-colour, raw umbre, on white paper 450 x 372 mm. Recto, upper right corner: 'dans les montagnes de la grande chartreuse'. Watermark no. 22.
EXHIBITIONS : Leiden 1916C, no. 71; The Hague 1930, I no. 75; Groningen 1931, no. 80; Groningen 1952, no. 58.
PROVENANCE : Sale Van der Vugt, Amsterdam 27.4.1745, p. 40, Portef. no. 12 (L. 618); — Sale Tersmitten, Amsterdam 23.9.1754, p. 97, Livre V (L. 844); Sale Della Faille Waerloos, Amsterdam 19.1.1904, no. 252; — Collection Hofstede de Groot, inv. no. 247, bequest 1914, no. 47; — Groninger Museum voor Stad en Lande, inv. no. 1931–179.

An album with thirty-two landscape drawings by Frederic Moucheron, 'vues de la grande Chartreuse', was sold at sale Van der Vugt at Amsterdam.¹ Nine years later, probably the same album, now containing thirty-one pieces,² appeared at sale Tersmitten³ and was bought by Huquier, the wellknown collector and art dealer from Paris. At two sales of the Huquier collection⁴ only 14 of the 31 drawings were sold, so probably 17 of them must have been sold previously,[5] the owner being a collector as well as a dealer. After that date, single pieces of the set can be found at various sales during the eighteenth and nineteenth century.[6] If we assume that this album contained all the marketable drawings from Moucheron's journey through the country surrounding Grenoble, our drawing must have been one of them, together with ca. thirty similar landscapes in public and private collections.[7] Moucheron stayed in France from 1655 until 1658, so we may assume that our drawing originates from this period.

[1] Sale H. van der Vugt, Amsterdam 27.4.1745, p. 40, Portef. no. 12: 'een Gebonde Boek met twee Afgezette Kaarten van de Chartireuse in Vrankrijk gelegen, met 32 Tekeningen na 't leven, van 't zelve, door den Ouden Moucheron, benevens het manuscript, wegens de Beschrijving van de zelve Order en Klooster, in het Latyn beschreven, op groot Mediaan.' [2] The missing drawing could have been no. 46, Kbk E, of sale Feitama, Amsterdam 16.10.1758: 'een gezicht in de wildernis bij Grenoble, omtrent 1670, 16⅓–14 dm, gekocht in 1745.' [3] Sale H. Tersmitten, Amsterdam 23.9.1754, p. 97, Livre V: 'Relié en Cuir Rouge forme d'Atlas contenant les Vues de la Grande Chartreuse, en trente et un Morceaux grands que moyens, dessinées d'apres nature par F. Moucheron. La plus grande partie de ces Desseins sont lavés, et quelques autres faits à la plume; ce Recueil est très capital et rare. On y a ajouté une grande Estampe enluminée qui contient le plan du tout ensemble. Comme ce volume est relié on le vendra en entier.' [4] Sale Huquier, Paris 1.7.1771, p. 16, no. 46: 'Cinq vues des environs de la grande Chartreuse, dessinées d'après nature par le vieux Moucheron. No. 47: Quatre autres vues, idem, par le même.' Sale Huquier, Paris 9.11.1772, no. 255: 'Deux vues de montagnes avec chute d'eau, près de la grande Chartreuse; dessein d'un beau détail, à la plume et à l'encre de la Chine, par Frédéric Moucheron; ils portent 16 poces de 6 lig. de haut, sur 21 pouc. 9 lig. de large.' No. 256: 'Trois vues des environs de Grenoble; desseins à la plume lavé à l'encre de la Chine, et rehaussé de blanc au pinceau, par le même.' No such drawings figured in the first sale of Huquier's collection, anonymous sale, Amsterdam 14.9.1761. [5] For instance, a drawing at sale Tjark, Amsterdam 10.11.1762, no. 238: 'Een lantschap na 't leven, in Savoye bij Grenoble, met de pen gewassen, hoog 11 breed 15 duim.' [6] Sale Paris, 24.4.1775, no. 36; sale Mariette, Paris 15.11.1775, no. 965; sale Neyman, Paris 8.7.1776, no. 552; sale C. Smitt, Amsterdam 4.12.1780, Kbk H, no. 494; sale F. W. Greebe, Amsterdam 8.12.1788, no. 13; sale W. P. Kops, Amsterdam 14.3.1808, Kbk E, no. 3; sale J. de Vos, Amsterdam 22.5.1883, no. 327. [7] Paris, Ecole des Beaux-Arts, Lugt 1950, no. 44, Pl. XLVII. Paris, Louvre, Lugt, 1929–33, I, no. 486, Pl. LXXX. Hamburg, Kunsthalle, inv. no. 22205, Bernt no. 422. Haarlem, Teylers Museum, cat. 1904, no. R34 and perhaps no. R33.

53. Pieter Mulier, the Younger (Cavaliere Tempesta), *Old house with climber*

p. 179

DATA: Black chalk, brown wash, on greyish paper 149 x 116 mm. Signed at the lower edge, in light brown ink: 'A:vOstade fecit'. Recto: owner's mark De Valori (Lugt 2500), partly removed. Watermark no. 23.

LITERATURE: Hirschmann, p. 210.

EXHIBITIONS: Groningen 1915, no. 39; Leiden 1916C, no. 74; The Hague 1930, I no. 76; Groningen 1931, no. 81; Groningen 1952, no. 60.

PROVENANCE: Sale De Valori, Paris 26.11.1907, no. 179; — Collection Hofstede de Groot, inv. no. 315, bequest 1914, no. 48; — Groninger Museum voor Stad en Lande, inv. no. 1931–180.

Bought by Hofstede de Groot as an Ostade, there has never been any dispute about the authorship of this drawing. Comparable pieces from Ostade's documented work's, however, are not easily found. The signature is not unlike Ostade's hand, but it is written in ink of a different colour from the wash. The technique of rough, black chalk with grey or bistre wash is associated rather with Pieter Mulier the younger, known as Cavaliere Tempesta,[1] of whom we know several similar drawings. First of all the beautiful view of a row of houses with a gateway,[2] inscribed in verso in an old hand: 'P.Mulier'. Very similar also is a drawing in Paris,[3] likewise inscribed 'Molier'. Attributed to Mulier is a view of a courtyard in the Louvre[4] which shows the same technique and subject matter as our drawing and the two other examples. In Haarlem,[5] there is a drawing of an old farm building, likewise in rough black chalk and bistre wash, which shows exactly the same wooden fence as can be seen in our drawing. We are convinced that a drawing in Besançon[6] must be credited to Mulier also, rather than to Roghman, as the present attribution suggests. Like many other artists, Mulier employed different tech-

Fig. 23. Pieter Mulier, *View of an old farm.* Drawing, Haarlem, Teylers Museum

niques according to the subject of his work. His pure landscape drawings are executed in a bold, romantic manner, not unlike Berchem and sometimes Molijn, whereas the views of old walls, courtyards and sheds are more comparable to Barend Gael's tone. Herman Saftleven also sometimes worked in this style.[7] Especially in this genre of rustic, ramshackle walls, commonplace as it may be, Mulier succeeds in expressing a sentiment that strikes us as being totally different from Ostade's drawings. Mulier shares with other Italianisants a predilection for sunlit, timeless moments, a distant echo of the serene calm of Arcadia, in contrast to Ostade's anecdotal jest.

[1] To Prof. Van Regteren Altena we owe the suggestion of Mulier's name in connection with the present drawing.   [2] Kaapstad, Suid-Afrikaanse Nasionale Kunsmuseum (coll. Michaelis, inv. no. 321.)   [3] Ecole des Beaux-Arts, Lugt 1950, no. 419, Pl. XLVI.   [4] Lugt, 1929–33, II, no. 490, Pl. LXXXIII.   [5] Teylers Museum, cat. 1904, no. R75. See fig. 23. Another drawing by this hand, attributed to Mulier, is in the museum Boymans–Van Beuningen: country-road with carts, inv. no. PM1.   [6] Musée des Beaux-Arts, inv. no. 2744, Photo Gernsheim no. 22051.   [7] Rotterdam, Museum Boymans-van Beuningen, inv. no. H56. Besançon, Musée des Beaux-Arts, inv. no. 292, landscape with a bridge, photo Gernsheim no. 16409.

54. Chrispijn van de Passe, *Cat, mouse and a lizard*   p. 180

DATA: Pen and bistre, on white paper 91 x 127 mm. Recto, in the shadow to the right of the cat, monogram ꝑ , owner's mark Esdaile (Lugt 2617). Verso, in pen and brown ink: '1801 WE P 48 N 25'.

LITERATURE: Henkel 1916, p. 340; Van Regteren Altena 1931, p. 71 and 72; Van Regteren Altena 1935, p. 56, note 2; Reznicek I, p. 44 note 41 and p. 485; Bol 1963, no. 28.

EXHIBITIONS: The Hague 1902, no. 20; Groningen 1915, no. 29; Leiden 1916A, no. 49; The Hague 1930, I no. 52; Groningen 1931, no. 58; The Hague 1955, no. 24; Paris 1960, no. 146.

PROVENANCE: Collection Esdaile 1801; Art dealer Van Gogh, Amsterdam 1901; — Collection Hofstede de Groot, inv. no. 69, bequest 1914, no. 32; — Groninger Museum voor Stad en Lande, inv. no. 1931–157.

In his catalogue of Golzius' drawings, Reznicek correctly attributed this small sheet to Chrispijn van de Passe, the Elder; until then it had passed under the name of Goltzius or De Gheyn. The well-known monogram of Van de Passe is scarcely visible in the shadow to the right of the cat. The cat, according to Reznicek, is a copy of the cat from Saenredam's etching after Goltzius (Bartsch 100). We have not been able to find a suitable explanation as to a possible allegorical significance, if indeed any such significance exists in the present drawing.

55. Rembrandt, *Old man, facing to the left* p. 181

DATA: Pen and bistre, grey and bistre wash, on brownish paper 152 x 132 mm. Signed in the lower right corner in a later hand: 'Rimbrandt'. Lower left corner: owner's mark De Valori (Lugt 2500), partly removed; pasted on paper, no visible watermark.

LITERATURE: Von Seidlitz, p. 253, no. 12; Hirschmann, p. 8; Benesch II, no. 270, fig. 295.

EXHIBITIONS: Amsterdam 1913, no. 53; Leiden 1916B, no. 2; The Hague 1930, I no. 85; Groningen 1931, no. 90.

PROVENANCE: Coll. Lippmann; Coll. Kleinberger; Sale De Valori, Paris 26.II.1907, no. 201; — Art dealer Obach & Co., London 1908; — Collection Hofstede de Groot, inv. no. 558, bequest 1914, no. 93; — Groninger Museum voor Stad en Lande, inv. no. 1931–189.

Apart from the alien hand responsible for the addition of the background and the little cap, to which Benesch[1] has drawn the attention, we are struck by the contrast between the head and the body. Benesch explains this contrast as follows: 'The roughly framed body forms a contrast to the head, but the character of the strong line work can be observed also in other drawings of about 1635'.[2] Prof. Van de Waal, however, remarks that this contrast is produced not only by means of the use of the light and the heavy pen, but also by a definite difference in scale. Notwithstanding the fact that we know 'the character of the strong line work' of the body from other drawings of ca. 1635, the quality is far inferior to that of Rembrandt. The hands lack a distinct construction and the man's right leg and left arm are wooden. It is difficult to reconcile this deficiency with the very 'subtle drawn head' that is 'closely comparable to nos. 267, bearded man in a high cap, London, British Museum, and 333, head of a man in a fur cap, Paris, Louvre'.[3]

The fact that there are several other comparable studies of heads[4] suggests that only the head of our drawing may have been executed by Rembrandt, whereas the body could well have been added by a pupil.

[1] Benesch II, no. 270, fig. 295. [2] Ibidem. [3] Ibidem. [4] Benesch II, nos. 268, 269, 329, 330 and 332.

56. Rembrandt, *Actor in the character of Pantalone* p. 182

DATA: Pen and bistre, on white paper 193 x 130 mm. Recto: owner's mark J. C. Robinson (Lugt 1433). Verso: small sketch in pen and bistre of a figure on horseback; owner's mark Von Lanna (Lugt 2773) and '298'. Watermark no. 24.

LITERATURE: Valentiner, no. 755*; Kossmann, opp. p. 91*; Hirschmann, p. 9*; Von Seidlitz, p. 253 no. L12; Valentiner 1925-26 p. 270* (erroneously as: Hamburg, Kunsthalle); Van Regteren Altena 1931, p. 71; Gudlaugsson, p. 29; Benesch II, no. 295, fig. 333; Sumowski, p. 5; Haverkamp Begemann, p. 23; Volskaja, p. 56.

EXHIBITIONS: Amsterdam 1913, no. 47; Leiden 1916B, no. 12; Paris 1921, no. 64; The Hague 1930, I no. 83; Groningen 1931, no. 88; Groningen 1952, no. 63; The Hague 1955, no. 37; Amsterdam/ Rotterdam 1956, no. 39; Brussels 1961, no. 59; Ingelheim 1964, no. 62; London 1964, no. 107; Prague 1966, no. 88; Paris 1967, no. 157*.

PROVENANCE: Coll. Sir Thomas Lawrence; — Art dealer Woodburn; — Sale Esdaile, London (Christie) 17.6.1840, no. 19? (L. 15863); Art dealer Woodburn?; Coll. Andrew James; — Coll. Miss James; — Sale J. C. Robinson, Amsterdam 20.11.1882, no. 175 (L. 42347); Sale Von Lanna, Stuttgart 6.5.1910, no. 467; — Collection Hofstede de Groot, inv. no. 354, bequest 1914, no. 91; — Groninger Museum voor Stad en Lande, inv. no. 1931–187.

By merely reproducing the present drawing in his book on the history of the Dutch theatre E. F. Kosman (see Bibliography) suggested for the first time that the figure might be an actor. S. Gudlaugsson and V. Volskaja (see Bibliography) identified the character as that of Pantalone, one of the chief personages from the *commedia dell'arte*.[1] In Hamburg there is a drawing[2] of the same actor, this time addressing a partner. We see the same man representing another character in a drawing in Frankfurt am Main.[3] Together with a number of other drawings representing scenes from the stage, our drawing is generally dated ca. 1635.

It would be of little avail to search for an event in the theatrical history of Amsterdam bearing a possible relationship to our drawing. G. Witkowski's enlightening article[4] on the relation between the Amsterdam theatre and Rembrandt strengthens us in this opinion. The gist of his thesis is that the images of the official stage differed essentially from the nature of the artist's vivid imagination. 'Stilistisch und technisch blieb die Schouwburg hinter dem gestaltenden Vermögen des Malers weit zurück' (p. 115). 'Selbst in den allegorischen Bildern und Radierungen, wo am ehesten wegen der Uebersetzung begrifflicher Vorstellungen in bildhafte Gestaltung eine Verwandtschaft zu vermuten wäre, schlägt Rembrandt ein völlig anderes Verfahren als die Sinnespelen und ihre Nachfolger ein. Dort gab es zwei Formen, Aufzug und vertooning, als primäre, aus denen dann ein mit Dialog ausgestattetes schwaches Agieren erwuchs. Dagegen beobachte man die innere Spannung, das dramatische Geschehen in Rembrandts Allegorien, wo das Begriffliche völlig in der Handlung sublimiert ist und in die Sphären individuellen Fühlens und Erlebens ausstrahlt ... Solchen Kompositionen fehlt jede Verwandtschaft mit den im Drama auftretenden mageren Sinnbildern, selbst denen in Hoofts *Gerard van Velzen*.' (p. 116-7). The influence of the stage on Rembrandt's work, if any,[5] can only be found on another level: 'Einzig die von Valentiner[6] wiedergegebenen Jahrmarkt-szenen erweisen—mit einiger Ausweitung des Begriffs des Theaters—die Teilnahme des Künstlers an solcher volkstümlicher Schau, freilich kaum mehr als das Verlangen, dort Bewegungsmotive festzuhalten' (p. 127).

W. Sumowski (see Bibliography) mentions a copy after our drawing, ex coll. Dalhousie, in

1930 in the Schever collection, Zürich. According to the tradition our drawing would have figured in a Thibaudeau sale; the only entry from the various Thibaudeau sales is the one[7] under the name of Oliver, 'Figure of a Man in a large hat and cloak, pen and ink; from the Paignon Dijonval, Lawrence and Russell Collections'.

[1] S. Gudlaugsson, *Ikonographische Studien über die holländische Malerei und das Theater des 17. Jahrhunderts*, Würzburg 1938, p. 32: 'Schon Rembrandt zeichnete den Faccanappa (das ist eine besondere Pantalonefigur, die durch einen sehr breiten flachen Hut gekennzeichnet ist), aber es sind nur zwei Einzelstudien, die nicht in erzählerischen Zusammenhang mit einem Bildganzen stehen.' [2] Kunsthalle. Benesch II, no. 296, fig. 334. [3] Städelsches Institut. Benesch II, no. 297, fig. 337. [4] See Bibliography. [5] See also J. Q. van Regteren Altena, 'Rembrandt und die Amsterdamer Bühne', in *Kunstchronik*, 1957, p. 135–137. [6] See Bibliography Valentiner 1925–6. [7] Sale A. W. Thibaudeau, London (Sotheby) 9.12.1889, no. 1108.

57. Rembrandt, *Saskia sitting up in bed*   p. 183

DATA: Pen and bistre, on white paper 149 x 190 mm.

LITERATURE: Valentiner, no. 688*; Valentiner 1923, p. 275; Becker, no. 28*; Göpel, p. 195*; Benesch 1935, p. 22; Benesch II, no. 282, fig. 315; Haverkamp Begemann, p. 22; Hekscher, p. 10.

EXHIBITIONS: The Hague 1930, I no. 105; Groningen 1931, no. 106; Groningen, 1948, no. 104; Haarlem 1951, no. 150; Groningen 1952, no. 64*; Amsterdam/Rotterdam 1956, no. 50; Washington 1958, no. 61.

PROVENANCE: Coll. Sir Thomas Lawrence; — Art dealer Woodburn; — Sale Esdaile, London (Christie) 17.6.1840, no. 16 (L. 15863); Sale Cremer, Amsterdam 15.6.1886, no. 258 (L. 45864); — Sale La Sablonière, Amsterdam 30.6.1891, no. 184 (L. 50126); — Sale C. Schöffer, Amsterdam 30.5.1893, no. 326 (L. 51799); Collection A. P. Vischer-Boelger, Basel (gift to Hofstede de Groot, Sept. 1921); — Collection Hofstede de Groot, inv. no. 676, bequest 1926; — Groninger Museum voor Stad en Lande, inv. no. 1931–205.

Ca. 1635 Rembrandt made a number of sketches[1] of Saskia, probably when she was in childbed (See Bibliography Valentiner 1923). Benesch draws our attention to the fact that 'the features of Saskia can be recognised with portrait-like precision'. In another drawing, in Budapest,[2] Saskia is represented seated before a window. It is difficult to understand how Benesch could accept our drawing and reject the one in Budapest. Though the poise of the head in the two drawings is different, there exists absolute conformity regarding the nature of the artist's image of Saskia. Also the means by which the image is expressed are exactly the same. No copyist, forger or pupil is capable of adopting the same disposition towards a model, and especially the subconscious mental and physical mechanism responsible for the expression of this disposition is inalienable. It therefore seems not unreasonable to accept the study in Budapest also as a Rembrandt. Professor Heckscher (see Bibliography) touches upon the pose of the *caput manui innixum*. 'Sleep, dream, melancholia, life contemplative, creative thought, inspiration, mourning—they could all be suggestively expressed by means of this particular gesture. The exact meaning can only be gathered if we are sure of the context in which the pose appears.' In this case the context is quite clear; Saskia in childbed, represented in a musing or pensive attitude, does not seem to be incompatible with the artist's own feelings towards the subject.

[1] Benesch II, no. 281, fig. 317. [2] Benesch II, A9: 'hardly drawn by Rembrandt himself. It is rather one of the most outstanding examples of Rembrandt's school.' A copy appeared at auction sale The Hague 1.3.1943, no. 132*.

58. Rembrandt?, *Woman lying in bed, and a nurse* p. 184

DATA: Pen and bistre, bistre wash, on brownisch paper 178 x 147 mm. Verso: owner's mark Stroganoff (Lugt 550).

LITERATURE: Valentiner, no. 698*; Teding van Berkhout, no. 20*; Von Seidlitz, p. 254, no. 165; Benesch II, no. 410, fig. 465.

EXHIBITIONS: Amsterdam 1913, no. 74; Leiden 1916B, no. 65; The Hague 1930, I no. 93; Groningen 1931, no. 94; Groningen 1952, no. 65; The Hague 1955, no. 41.

PROVENANCE: Sale Esdaile, London (Christie) 18.6.1840, no. 1046 (L. 15865); Coll. Stroganoff, Rome. — Art dealer Colnaghi, London; — Art dealer Strölin, Paris; — Collection Hofstede de Groot, inv. no. 519, bequest 1914, no. 101; — Groninger Museum voor Stad en Lande, inv. no. 1931–193.

The situation that we see in the present drawing is known from other drawings of the same subject.[1] For us, this is the only reason why Rembrandt's name, though questionably, is still linked with the drawing, because the style and quality alone would certainly lead one to think of the figure drawings of Philips Koninck.[2] The two profiles, the hatching and the quick drawing in general have much in common with Koninck's technique.[3] If the drawing actually was executed by Rembrandt, it is just this kind of drawing that was the example which Koninck was never able to get away from in his figure-drawings.

[1] Benesch II, no. 405, fig. 461, Munich, Graphische Sammlung. The difference lies in the changed standpoint from which the scene is seen. Prof. Van Regteren Altena suggests that in the present drawing, made in the evening, a candle would be standing on the mantelpiece, to the left of the women. [2] Even the theme is not necessarily an indication of Rembrandt's authorship; Koninck also made a few drawings representing family scenes: Rotterdam, Museum Boymans-van Beuningen, Cat. 1869, no. 641, Hofstede de Groot 1906, no. 1380 as Rembrandt; Coll. F. Lugt, Paris, Gerson 1936, no. 240, signed, formerly coll. Fairfax Murray (sale London 30.1.1920, no. 115). [3] See for instance: Rotterdam, Museum Boymans-van Beuningen, inv. no. PHK3. Also a drawing at auction sale Boreel, Amsterdam 15.6.1908, no. 496, Gerson 1936, no. Z183 (earlier at sale Artaria, Wien 6.5.1896, no. 1013, as Rembrandt), recto and verso.

59. Rembrandt, *Isaac blessing Jacob* p. 185

DATA: Pen and bistre, bistre wash, white body-colour, on white paper 125 x 173 mm. Pasted on paper, no visible watermark.

LITERATURE: Valentiner, no. 62*; Kauffmann, p. 175 (note); Benesch 1935, p. 35; Parker, p. 74; Benesch III, no. 508, fig. 632; Rotermund, p. 17*; *Rembrandt drawings for the Bible*, no. 9*.

EXHIBITIONS: The Hague 1930, I no. 96; Groningen 1931, no. 96; Groningen 1948, no. 102; Groningen 1952, no. 67; The Hague 1955, no. 36.

PROVENANCE: Coll. Barnard; — Coll. Reynolds; — Coll. Lawrence, 1835; — Sale Esdaile, London (Christie) 18.5.1840, no. 47 (L. 15865); — Sale Woodburn, London (Christie) 4.6.1860, no. 778 (L. 25634); Art dealer Colnaghi; — Sale London 20.7.1914, no. 44; — Sale Hilgrove Cox, London 8.3.1922, no. 62; — Art dealer 'Hollandsche Kunsthandel', Amsterdam 1923; — Collection Hofstede de Groot, inv. no. 788, bequest 1926; — Groninger Museum voor Stad en Lande, inv. no. 1931–195.

In Berlin[1] is a copy of our drawing. Other versions of the theme are edited and reproduced by Benesch III, nos. 507, 509 and 510 (figs. 631, 634 and 633). These drawings, ours included, are generally dated 1640–42. Twenty years later, Rembrandt did another version of the theme.[2]

[1] Kupferstichkabinett, Cat. Bock-Rosenberg I, 1930, p. 245, inv. no. 8513; Hofstede de Groot 1906, no. 24.
[2] New York, The Frick collection; Benesch V, no. 1065, fig. 1284.

60. Rembrandt, *Samson and Delilah* p. 94

DATA: Pen and bistre, bistre wash, white body-colour, on white paper 190 x 233 mm. Watermark: Crowned Eagle.

LITERATURE: Valentiner, no. 142*; Becker, *Neue Folge,* no. 24*; Kauffmann, p. 162, 163, 173, 176*; Benesch 1935, p. 36; *O.K.W. Mededelingen* no. 23, 1956, p. 16*; Scheidig, no. 54*; Benesch III, no. 530, fig. 659; Rotermund, no. 87, p. 93*; *O.K.W. Mededelingen* no. 28, 1964, p. 48*.

EXHIBITIONS: The Hague 1930, I no. 98; Groningen 1931, no. 98; Groningen 1952, no. 66; The Hague 1955, no. 35; Amsterdam/Rotterdam 1956, no. 79*; Recklinghausen 1960, no. DII2; Amsterdam 1964, no. 68*.

PROVENANCE: Sale Argoutinsky, Amsterdam 12.12.1922, no. 1903; — Collection Hofstede de Groot, inv. no. 692, bequest 1926; — Groninger Museum voor Stad en Lande, inv. no. 1931-197.

In the entry of the catalogue Amsterdam 1964[1] the drawing is placed in its iconographical and stylistic relation to other works: the composition is derived from the painting of 1628.[2] Most of the critics[3] place the drawing between 1634 and 1640. In Leiden[4] there is another version of the theme, where Samson is represented in a similar position, seen from a different angle; the style of drawing, however, is totally different.

A drawing like the present one deserves our attention in more ways than one, as it is able to convey a remarkably direct insight into the artist's mind and as it makes us realize the uniqueness of Rembrandt's creative process. The complete lack of inhibition with which Rembrandt chooses the unsophisticated, contrary to the generally held idealizing tendencies in art, makes this drawing a valuable document.

[1] Written by Miss L. J. C. Frerichs; see List of Exhibitions. [2] Berlin, Staatliche Museen, cat. 1962, no. 812A.
[3] Valentiner: ca. 1634; Kauffmann: 1637–38; H. Gerson: 1636–40; cat. Amsterdam/Rotterdam 1956: ca. 1635–38; F. Lugt: ca. 1635–40; Haverkamp Begemann: 1638. [4] Printroom of the University, Benesch IV, no. A35, fig. 1034.

61. Rembrandt, *Scene from the Old Testament* p. 186

DATA: Pen and bistre, bistre wash, on white paper 204 x 315 mm. Verso, in an old hand (sanguine): 'Rembrandt'.

LITERATURE: Valentiner, no. 576*; Valentiner 1925–26, p. 265*. Hofstede de Groot 1906, no. 186; Hofstede de Groot 1929, p. 141*; Benesch 1935, p. 42; Benesch III, no. 596, fig. 726; Witkowski, p. 122 and 126*; Drost, p. 190*.

EXHIBITIONS: The Hague 1930, I no. 103; Groningen 1931, no. 103; Groningen 1948, no. 100; Haarlem 1951, no. 169; Groningen 1952, no. 72; The Hague 1955, no. 38; Brussels 1961, no. 54.

PROVENANCE: Coll. W. von Bode, Berlin; — Coll. L. Levin, Breslau; Art dealer Nebehay, Vienna 1926; — Collection Hofstede de Groot, inv. no. 960, bequest 1926; — Groninger Museum voor Stad en Lande, inv. no. 1931-202.

60. Rembrandt, *Samson and Delilah*

Valentiner was the first to interpret the scene as The Roman women before Coriolanus (Livy 2. 40).[1] Benesch gives the drawing the same title without any comment.[2] G. Witkowski (see Bibliography) and the catalogue of the exhibition in Brussels 1961 criticize this interpretation, with reference to a drawing in the Koch collection,[3] doubtless a representation of the subject of Coriolanus and misinterpreted by Benesch as David and Abigail; because of his oriental costume and his age, the man in our drawing could hardly be Coriolanus. Apart from this, the onlooker, half-hidden in the rocks, is not reported in Livy's account of the story. It is probable that a story from the Old Testament is represented here. W. Drost (see Bibliography) suggested that the composition may have been derived from a drawing by Adam Elsheimer[4] of an unidentified subject: a number of men and women with children are approaching a man of distinguished appearance. We do not think that there is a convincing similarity in the two compositions, but the subjects could well stem from the same source; Rembrandt often shares his themes with the group that we usually label as the 'pre-rembrandtists'.

[1] See Bibliography Valentiner 1925–6: a performance of Shakespeare's *Coriolanus* might have stimulated Rembrandt to draw the present scene. This supposition, however, is not elaborated by the author.   [2] Benesch III, no. 596, fig. 726.   [3] London; Valentiner, no. 813; ca. 1656; Benesch V, no. 1013, fig. 1229.   [4] Paris, Louvre. Cat. Louis Demonts, t. II, 1938, no. 552*.

62. Rembrandt, *The daughters of Cecrops finding Erichthoneus* p. 187

DATA: Pen and bistre, body-white, on white paper 175 x 219 mm.

LITERATURE: Hofstede de Groot 1906, no. 42; Valentiner, no. 597*; *Dessins de Rembrandt*, no. 42*; Teding van Berkhout, no. 13*; Von Seidlitz 1917, p. 254, no. 167; Hirschmann, p. 17; Lippmann-HdG, 4th series II, no. 96*; Benesch 1935, p. 42; Scheidig, no. 84*; Benesch III, no. 623, fig. 753; Stechov 1963, p. 27 ff.

EXHIBITIONS: Amsterdam 1913, no. 38; Leiden 1916B, no. 67; The Hague 1930, I no. 82; Groningen 1931, no. 87; Groningen 1948, no. 103; Groningen 1952, no. 74.

PROVENANCE: Sale Schöffer, Amsterdam 30.5.1893, no. 328 (L. 51799); Sale Boreel a.o., Amsterdam 15.6.1908, no. 483; — Collection Hofstede de Groot, inv. no. 353, bequest 1914 no. 90; — Groninger Museum voor Stad en Lande, inv. no. 1931–186.

Erichthoneus was the son of Hephaistos and Gaea. Placed in a chest by Athena, he was given in custody to Aglauros, Pandrosos and Herse, the three daughters of Cecrops. When they disregarded Athena's interdiction against opening the chest and saw that the child's feet had the form of snakes, they went mad and killed themselves. Wolfgang Stechow (see Bibliography) believes that Antonio Tempesta's etching of the same subject[1] influenced Rembrandt, and gives also an account of versions of the theme by other artists. The illustrations in some of the later editions of Ovid's *Metamorphoses*, however, could also have played a part in the development. Though there is a vast difference in the arrangement of the figures of the three women, the compositional principle of the woodcut from the Antwerp edition of 1619[2] has a distant echo in Rembrandt's drawing. The high building to the left and the place of the chest have been repeated. The particular element, however, that would have appealed to Rembrandt's vigorous imagination, the 'jumpy' movement of the women, has been endowed with his own, less rhetorical vision. It is interesting to note how the artist completely by-passes the moralizing tendencies of the story. Rembrandt is concerned exclusively with the actual happening, with a visual greed comparable to that of the spectator of a contemporary 'klucht-spel',[3] full of coarse practical jokes. The influence of Pieter Lastman's compositions is also clearly apparent. The startled women in the two versions of Odysseus and Nausicaa show the same kind of movement. Drawings like the present one reveal what Rembrandt gained by his apprenticeship with Lastman, i.e. the truest possible expression of intense emotion.

Rembrandt treated the same subject in another drawing[4], now in a private collection in America. Valentiner dates our version (erroneously given as figuring at sale Berlin

Fig. 24. Woodcut illustration from Ovid's *Metamorphosis* etc., Antwerpen, 1619

25.5.1908, no. 418) about 1645, Benesch about 1648–9 and Von Seidlitz in the first half of the fifties. There are no doubts regarding the authenticity of the drawing. The lid of the basket has been drawn twice and corrected with body-white.

[1] Number 14 of the series Bartsch 638–787, reproduced with Stechow, Pl. XIV, 2. [2] *Metamorphosis*, etc., Antwerpen, 1619, boek II, p. 30 (see fig. 24) shows a rather clumsy copy of *Schöne Figuren aus dem... Poeten Ovidio, etc.*, by Johann Posthium von Germersheim, Frankfurt a.M. 1569, p. 28, in its turn a reversed copy of the illustration of the French edition *La Metamorphose d'Ovide figurée,* à Lyon, 1564, p. e9 verso, which was also used in *Pub. Ovidii Nasonis Metamorphoseon Libri XV,* Paris, 1578, p. 86–7. [3] Low comedy. [4] Sale Berlin (Amsler & Ruthard) 25.5.1908, no. 418; Benesch I, no. 150, fig. 166.

63. Rembrandt, *The departure of the prodigal son*   p. 188

DATA: Pen and bistre, grey wash, on white paper 149 x 232 mm.

LITERATURE: Hofstede de Groot 1906, no. 818; Valentiner, no. 384*; Hirschmann 1917, p. 17; Becker, no. 33*; De Vries Lam*; Benesch III, no. 651, fig. 788.

EXHIBITIONS: Amsterdam 1913, no. 28; Leiden 1916B, no. 66; The Hague 1930, I no. 91; Groningen 1931, no. 92.

PROVENANCE: Coll. Sir Henry Hawley; Sale London (Christie) 16.7.1891, no. 206? (L. 50151); Fourth sale Sedelmeyer, Paris 12.6.1907, no. 280; — Art dealer A. Löbl, Paris; — Collection Hofstede de Groot, inv. no. 516, bequest 1914, no. 99; — Groninger Museum voor Stad en Lande, inv. no. 1931–191.

Several scholars have expressed doubts concerning the authenticity of the present drawing (Valentiner, Lugt, Gerson, Van de Waal). Benesch accepts the line drawing as Rembrandt: 'The washes which give the drawing an entirely alien and weak character are by another hand.' Hofstede de Groot catalogued the drawing as The good Samaritan. This interpretation has been abandoned, as The departure of the prodigal son seems more adequate. The young man is obviously receiving money rather than paying the innkeeper.

64. Rembrandt, *Study of a standing woman and the heads of two men*   p. 189

DATA: Pen and bistre, on brownish paper 117 x 113 mm. Recto: owner's mark Rodrigues (Lugt 897).

LITERATURE: *Dessins de Rembrandt*, no. 24*; Lippmann-HdG, 4th series II, no. 98*; Van Regteren Altena 1931, p. 71*; Benesch IV, no. 731, fig. 874.

EXHIBITIONS: Amsterdam 1913, no. 61; Groningen 1915, no. 51; Leiden 1916B, no. 54; The Hague 1930, I no. 84; Groningen 1931, no. 89; Groningen 1952, no. 75; The Hague 1955, no. 40.

PROVENANCE: Collection E. Rodrigues. Anonymous sale, Paris 6.5.1909, no. 114*; — Collection Hofstede de Groot, inv. no. 356, bequest 1914, no. 92; — Groninger Museum voor Stad en Lande, inv. no. 1931–188.

The drawings to which Benesch refers for stylistic comparison appear to have been chosen rather arbitrarily, except for the first one (IV, no. 755, fig. 896). We expect to see the same old man with his forked beard like the upper one in a study in Rotterdam.[1] Also the sweeping, supple lines of the figure of the woman are to be found there. The two men with their typical headgear also appear on a study in black chalk, from the Heseltine sale.[2] Studies like these seem to have been used for the 'Honderd guldens prent' (Bartsch 74) of 1649. Most scholars date the drawing in the last few years before 1650.

[1] Museum Boymans-van Beuningen, Koenigs collection, inv. no. R29. Benesch IV, no. 704, fig. 842.   [2] Amsterdam 27.5.1913, no. 9. Benesch IV, no. 720, fig. 863.

65. Rembrandt, *Farm-house with a clump of trees to the right*   p. 190

DATA: Pen and bistre, grey wash, on brownish paper 117 x 193 mm. Recto: owner's mark Zoomer (Lugt 1511). Inscription 'Rembrandt' on the lower right side removed. Watermark no. 25.

LITERATURE: Valentiner, no. 1220; Benesch IV, no. 841, fig. 988.

EXHIBITIONS: Leiden 1916B, no. 52; The Hague 1930, I no. 87; Groningen 1931, no. 107; Groningen 1948, no. 106.

PROVENANCE: Coll. J. P. Zoomer, Amsterdam; Art dealer Strölin, Paris 1913; — Collection Hofstede de Groot, inv. no. 547, bequest 1914, no. 103; — Groninger Museum voor Stad en Lande, inv. no. 1931–206.

Benesch and Valentiner accept the drawing as a Rembrandt. The former gives the date as 1648–50: '... After 1650 Rembrandt would never have made the same shower of diagonal hatchings sweep over the front and side wall of a building as we see it here, because this procedure flattens its cubic quality instead of emphasizing it.' In this case, it is especially difficult to be definite regarding the authenticity. The conception of the scene, however, gives evidence of a strong and uniting vision so that, notwithstanding obvious weaknesses in the drawing of the road and the roof of the house, Rembrandt's authorship seems plausible.

66. Rembrandt, *An Oriental, standing* p. 191

DATA: Pen and bistre, on brownish paper 142 x 74 mm. Lower right corner: removed owner's mark. Glued on paper, no visible watermark.

LITERATURE: Hirschmann, p. 18; Von Seidlitz, p. 254, no. L42; Benesch 1935, p. 56; Benesch V, no. 1130, fig. 1353; Van der Grinten, thesis no. 6.

EXHIBITIONS: Amsterdam 1913, no. 55; Groningen 1915, no. 48; Leiden 1916B, no. 42; Paris 1921, no. 65; The Hague 1930, I no. 78; Groningen 1931, no. 83; Groningen 1952, no. 76.

PROVENANCE: Sale Duval, Amsterdam 22.6.1910, no. 305; — Collection Hofstede de Groot, inv. no. 345, bequest 1914, no. 86; — Groninger Museum voor Stad en Lande, inv. no. 1931–182.

Benesch's comment upon the present drawing seems plausible: 'The delicate structure of the figure is seemingly influenced by the copies after Indian miniatures which Rembrandt did about that time (i.e. ca. 1656) and shortly before. The expression of the face might suggest that this figure is a study for an Ahasuerus in fury.' Originally, the figure may have been shorter. The shoulder-line has been corrected and consequently the arms. Particularly noticeable are the corrections made to the man's left arm. As always the question of authenticity poses itself. Benesch seems to rely in his judgement on the similarity with the copies after the Indian miniatures. The Rembrandtesque nature of the suggestion of the man's character is familiar to us from the documented oeuvre of the master. Rembrandt's forceful, slightly vulgarizing spirit manifests itself clearly, radiating from this little sketch. The comparison with a similar drawing by Nicolaes Maes[1] only stresses the superiority of our drawing.

[1] Amsterdam, Rijksprentenkabinet, inv. no. '30:42, M. D. Henkel, 1942, no. 5*.

67. Rembrandt, *Landscape with farm-house and a rolling horse* p. 192

DATA: Pen and bistre, bistre wash, on brown prepared paper 105 x 177 mm.

LITERATURE: Von Seidlitz, p. 254, no. L68; Hirschmann, p. 21*; Becker, *Neue Folge,* no. 28*; Valentiner 1931, p. 140*; Benesch 1935, p. 48; Benesch II, no. 1225, fig. 1444; Haverkamp Begemann, p. 85.

EXHIBITIONS: Amsterdam 1913, no. 85; Leiden 1916B, no. 68; The Hague 1930, I no. 90; Groningen 1931, no. 111; Groningen 1948, no. 108; Groningen 1952, no. 69; The Hague 1955, no.42.

PROVENANCE: Sale Obreen a.o., Amsterdam 4.12.1912, no. 378; — Collection Hofstede de Groot, inv. no. 515, bequest 1914, no. 98; — Groninger Museum voor Stad en Lande, inv. no. 1931–210.

This beautiful landscape has been commented upon frequently. Benesch regarded it as 'sketch (in reverse) preparatory to the etching of 1650, Bartsch no. 224.'[1] As there are, however, considerable differences, we would prefer to re-phrase this statement, saying that the motif of the present drawing, obviously a sketch after nature, might possibly have lingered in Rembrandt's memory when he made the etching. Several suggestions have also been made about the topographical situation. Lugt[2] identifies the etching as the Diemerdijk between Houtewael and Zeeburg. Valentiner[3] identifies it as the farm in another drawing in New York.[4] The square tower to the right could be the same as in a drawing in the Koenigs collection in Rotterdam.[5]

According to Benesch[6] and Lugt, the wash is by another hand. If one considers a high quality as the guarantee of Rembrandt's authorship, then there is little doubt that the master executed our drawing. Apart from the high quality, however, the present landscape shows an absolute similarity in conception with the landscapes that Rembrandt depicted in his etchings. The greater the artist, the more powerful will be the personal flavour with which a landscape, taken from nature, is depicted. Rembrandt's unconditional acceptance of everyday reality is one of the most characteristic features of his conception. In this case there probably was no question of 'own invention'; the present landscape seems to be drawn entirely after nature. But even when Rembrandt composes a landscape or romanticizes it, he still composes or romanticizes everyday life, without altogether following the heroic ideals of his time. Also in the case of the present landscape we seem to feel the firm grasp of the artist on the things that fixed itself upon his vision.

[1] Benesch VI, no. 1225, fig. 1444. Haverkamp Begemann, in his comment on Benesch's corpus (see Bibliography) rejected this supposition. [2] F. Lugt, *Mit Rembrandt in Amsterdam,* Berlin, 1920, fig. 86, p. 137–9. [3] See Bibliography, Valentiner 1931. [4] Metropolitain Museum of Art, inv. no. 76436, ex. coll. Havemeyer. Benesch VI, no. 1271, fig. 1498. The catalogue of the exhibition 'Rembrandt drawings from American collections', New York/Harvard 1960, in which this drawing is included under no. 50, gives a negative judgement regarding this report: 'Valentiner's passing suggestion that the same farm is represented in a drawing at Groningen (Benesch 1225) is not really convincing.' [5] Museum Boymans-van Beuningen, inv. no. R100, Benesch VI, no. 1334, fig. 1570. [6] Ibidem.

68. Rembrandt, *Farm-house with a water-mill surrounded by trees*   p. 193

DATA: Pen and bistre, bistre wash, white body-colour, on brown prepared paper 160 x 240 mm. Recto: owner's mark J. P. Zoomer (Lugt 1511). Verso: owner's mark Heseltine (Lugt 1507).

LITERATURE: Hofstede de Groot 1906, no. 1055; Von Seidlitz, p. 252, no. 1055; Michel, p. 583; Lippmann-HdG, 1st series I, no. 40; Van Regteren Altena 1931, p. 71; Benesch 1935, p. 48; Benesch VI, no. 1247, fig. 1473.

EXHIBITIONS: Amsterdam 1898, no.?; London 1899, no. 149; Amsterdam 1913, no. 86; Leiden 1916B, no. 51; The Hague 1930, I no. 107; Groningen 1931, no. 108; Groningen 1952, no. 68; The Hague 1955, no. 39; Amsterdam/Rotterdam 1956, no. 167; Washington 1958, no. 66.

PROVENANCE: Coll. J. P. Zoomer; Sale Lawrence, London 1.7.1835, no. 64 (see L. 2446); — Sale Esdaile, London 17.6.1840, no. 119 (L. 15865); — Sale Woodburn, London 12.6.1860, no. 1501 (L. 25649); — Sale Grahame, London (Sotheby) 15.3.1878, no. 134 (L. 38136); Coll. Heseltine, cat. 1907, no. 28*; — Art dealer Colnaghi, London 1913; — Collection Hofstede de Groot, inv. no. 512, bequest 1914, no. 95; — Groninger Museum voor Stad en Lande, inv. no. 1931–207.

Benesch[1] gives a large number of landscape studies, comparable to the present drawing from a stylistic point of view. This entire group could have been made ca. 1650–51. Also in the catalogue of the exhibition in Washington 1958–59 the drawing is dated ca. 1650. The same entry speaks of 'Rembrandt's remarkable gift of realizing a perfectly balanced arrangement and thereby bestowing grandeur upon an otherwise humble subject.' In view of the obvious relevancy of this remark and of what has been said of the preceding drawing (no. 67), we have no doubt as to the authorship of Rembrandt.

[¹] Benesch VI, no. 1247, fig. 1473.

69. Rembrandt, *Cottages and trees on the embankment of a canal, a roller-bridge in the distance* p. 103

DATA: Pen and bistre wash, on brown prepared paper 110 x 148 mm. Owner's mark Richardson (Lugt 2184). Glued on paper, no visible watermark. On the mount, recto: owner's mark Heseltine (Lugt 1507), owner's mark Esdaile (Lugt 2617). Verso: 'Formerly in Richardson's coll.' 'R. Willet's coll. 1808 WE P 84 no. 130 Rembrandt'.

LITERATURE: Hofstede de Groot 1906, no. 1045; Michel, p. 583; Lippmann-HdG, 2nd series I, no. 32A*; Von Seidlitz, p. 252, no. 1045; Becker, *Neue Folge,* no. 29*; Van Regteren Altena 1931, p. 71*; Wimmer, p. 38; Benesch 1935, p. 57; Benesch VI, no. 1291, fig. 1520.

EXHIBITIONS: London 1899, no. 122; Amsterdam 1913, no. 88; Leiden 1916B, no. 72; Paris 1921, no. 69; The Hague 1930, I no. 89; Groningen 1931, no. 110; Groningen 1948, no. 105; Haarlem 1951, no. 178; Groningen 1952, no. 70; The Hague 1955, no. 45; Vancouver 1958, no. 61*; Washington 1958, no. 69.

PROVENANCE: Coll. J. Richardson Sr.; Coll. R. Willet, 1808; Coll. Lawrence; Sale Esdaile, London 17.6.1840, no. 60 (L. 15865); Sale C. S. Bale, London (Christie) 9.6.1881, no. 2431 (L. 41193); — Coll. J. P. Heseltine, cat. 1907, no. 44*; — Art dealer Colnaghi, London 1913; — Collection Hofstede de Groot, inv. no. 514, bequest 1914, no. 97; — Groninger Museum voor Stad en Lande, inv. no. 1931–209.

Fig. 25. Copy after Rembrandt, *Cottages and trees on the embankment of a canal, a roller-bridge in the distance.* Munich, Graphische Sammlung

There are several drawings of the same roller-bridge, one of these being the Lievens copy in this collection (no. 48). The present sketch has been made from a point somewhat further away. In Munich[1] there is another version; we do not think this is a copy after our drawing, as there are slight differences; it may well be, however, a copy after another, a lost original by Rembrandt. Also the possibility remains that a pupil accompanied Rembrandt on a trip and that both artists made a sketch of the same scene. In the Dutuit collection[2] there is another drawing of the roller-bridge, according to the entry in F. Lugt's catalogue[3] also by Rembrandt. The buildings to the right, however, are not the same as those in the present drawing and in the one in Munich. Perhaps here the roller-bridge is seen from the other side.

The comparison of the various versions of the same scene is not only interesting because of the topography, though. The effect of Rembrandt's eloquence upon our minds is generally concealed from our conscious knowledge because of its self-evident nature. We become aware of this effect, however, in a case like this where comparison is possible. The triviality of the other drawings is transformed in our study into a great monumentality by the means of an abbreviate way of drawing. The disposition of the scene has gained an unassailable logic that should not be confused with what we call reality; for in the world of the pictorial arts there is no reality, only vision.

[1] Graphische Sammlung, inv. no. 1412, see fig. 25.   [2] Petit Palais, Paris.   [3] Lugt 1927, no. 61, Pl. XXXI.

70. Rembrandt, *A small inn and sheds near a group of trees*   p. 194

DATA: Pen and bistre, bistre wash, on brownish paper 129 x 177 mm. Watermark no. 26.
LITERATURE: Benesch VI, no. 1330, fig. 1564; Lambourne, no. 47*.
EXHIBITIONS: Paris 1922, no. 3; The Hague 1930, I no. 95; Groningen 1931, no. 112; Groningen 1948, no. 107; Vancouver 1958, no. 62.
PROVENANCE: Sale Mathey, Paris 28.II.1924, no. 76*; — Collection Hofstede de Groot, inv. no. 910, bequest 1926; — Groninger Museum voor Stad en Lande, inv. no. 1931–211.

The possibility advanced by Benesch that a drawing in London[1] represents the same inn from a more remote standpoint on the road, seems very plausible. It is even possible to identify the place, with the aid of Rademaker's *Kabinet*,[2] as Houtewael near Amsterdam. Benesch dates the drawing ca. 1653–54. Also in this quick sketch, something is visible of Rembrandt's forceful cogency of which we have to become aware before the merits of the drawing can be fully understood.

[1] British Museum, cat. Hind, no. 106, Benesch VI, no. 1329, fig. 1563.   [2] Abraham Rademaker, *Kabinet van Nederlandsche Outheden en Gezichten,* etc., Amsterdam 1725, Vol. I, nos. 3 and 4.

71. Rembrandt?, *Striding angel*   p. 195

DATA: Pen and bistre, on white paper 157 x 66 mm.
LITERATURE: Hirschmann, p. 15*; Von Seidlitz, p. 254, no. L70; Benesch VI, c62.
EXHIBITIONS: Groningen 1915, no. 53; Leiden 1916B, no. 70; The Hague 1930, I no. 94; Groningen 1931, no. 95.

PROVENANCE: Sale Klinkosch, Vienna 15.4.1889, no. 713 (L. 48170). — Sale Freund, Amsterdam 2.12.1913, no.? — Art dealer Van Huffel, Utrecht 1913; — Collection Hofstede de Groot, inv. no. 521, bequest 1914, no. 102; — Groninger Museum voor Stad en Lande, inv. no. 1931–194.

In general, the drawing is not considered to be by Rembrandt, probably because of some weaknesses in the drawing. Benesch catalogues it as 'copy of an unknown original about 1650.' Yet in the purposefulness of the Angel's stride we find the expression of an Old Testament serenity, the intensity of which reminds us of other such scenes[1] by Rembrandt.

[1] Hagar and Ishmael in the desert, Hamburg, Kunsthalle, inv. no. 22411, Benesch V, no. 904, fig. 1117; Abel slain by Cain, Copenhagen Kobberstiksamling, Benesch V, no. 860, fig. 1069.

72. School of Rembrandt, *Woman kneeling before a bearded old man*

p. 196

DATA: Pen and bistre, on white paper 166 x 193 mm. Sketch of the same woman in the upper right corner and strokes of pen and bistre to the left side removed.

EXHIBITIONS: Amsterdam 1913, no. 15; The Hague 1930, I no. 100; Groningen 1931, no. 100.
PROVENANCE: Collection Dalhousie; — Art dealer Colnaghi, London 1922; — Art dealer Cassirer, Berlin 1923; — Collection Hofstede de Groot, inv. no. 884, bequest 1926; — Groninger Museum voor Stad en Lande, inv. no. 1931–199.

The quality does not permit attribution of this drawing to Rembrandt or even to one of his known pupils. The scene has been said[1] te represent Simeon in the temple. Rotermund[2] has suggested as the subject of a similar drawing, Elijah and the widow of Sarepta (I Kings 17). Lugt's opinion[3] that the drawing may be an old copy of ca. 1635 seems plausible; see for comparison The raising of the daughter of Jairus.[4]

[1] Catalogue of the exhibition The Hague 1930. [2] Rotermund, p. 103, no. 122, speaking about a drawing in Basel, private coll. Benesch VI, add. 11, fig. 1718. [3] As expressed in his Rembrandt-archive in The Hague, Rijksbureau voor Kunsthistorische Documentatie. [4] Berlin, coll. Rathenau. Benesch I, no. 62, fig. 70.

73. School of Rembrandt, *Jacob kneeling in prayer*   p. 197

DATA: Pen and bistre, on white paper 135 x 113 mm. Owner's mark Reynolds (Lugt 2364).
LITERATURE: Teding van Berkhout, no. 2; Von Seidlitz, p. 253, no. 116; Lugt 1933, no. 1215; Benesch II, no. C 26, fig. 563.
EXHIBITIONS: Amsterdam 1913, no. 3; Groningen 1915, no. 47; Leiden 1916B, no. 16; The Hague 1930, I no. 77; Groningen 1931, no. 82.
PROVENANCE: Collection Sir Joshua Reynolds; Art dealer Schnell, Paris 1910; — Collection Hofstede de Groot, inv. no. 344, bequest 1914, no. 85; — Groninger Museum voor Stad en Lande, inv. no. 1931–181.

The opinions regarding this drawing are unanimous. Benesch[1] and Lugt[2] both consider it as a copy after a lost original, of ca. 1936. Another copy after the same unknown drawing is in the Louvre.[3] A third version, a forgery after our study, appeared at a recent sale.[4]

69. Rembrandt, *Cottages and trees on the embankment of a canal, a roller-bridge in the distance*

[¹] II, no. C26, fig. 563.   [²] Lugt 1933, no. 1215*.   [³] See also Lugt's elaboration on the iconographical possibilities of the drawing, in the Louvre cat., mentioned in note 2.   [⁴] Amsterdam (Herzberger) 13.11.1962, no. 426. Even the collectionmark of Sir Joshua Reynolds has been copied.

74. School of Rembrandt, *The star of the Kings* p. 198

DATA: Pen and bistre, on white paper 194 x 194 mm. Recto, in the lower left corner, partly cut off: owner's mark Reynolds (Lugt 2364). Lower right corner: owner's mark Richardson (Lugt 2170). Watermark no. 27.

EXHIBITIONS: The Hague 1930, I no. 106; Groningen 1931, no. 104.

PROVENANCE: Coll. J. Richardson Jr., London 1772; Coll. Th. Hudson, London; Coll. Sir Joshua Reynolds; — Coll. Marchioness of Thomond; Coll. Lord Lucas (see Lugt 1696); — Sale Lady Lucas, London 29.6.1926, no. 36*; — Collection Hofstede de Groot, inv. no. 972 bequest 1926; — Groninger Museum voor Stad en Lande, inv. no. 1931–203.

Another version is in Warsaw.¹ The theme of both these drawings is connected with a sketch by Rembrandt in London.² In the drawings in Warsaw and Groningen, we are standing to the right of the door. In London the same scene, only with more figures, is depicted from a point of view to the left of the door. Several details are similar. The boy holding the star and the group of women in the doorway both occur in the London drawing and in the two identical versions in Warsaw and Groningen.

Following Benesch's supposition³ concerning the drawing in Warsaw, we believe that our drawing is another copy after the same lost original, which must have been a companion piece to the drawing in London.

Lord Lucas may have bought our drawing at one of the last sales in 1821 of the collection of Sir Joshua Reynolds, whose collection mark was partly cut off by Hofstede de Groot.

[¹] Formerly Royal Collection. Now in the University Library, Dept. of Prints and Drawings, inv. no. T174, no. 311. Benesch VI, addenda no. C4, fig. 1733. Exh. Warschau 1956, no. 93.   [²] The British Museum, cat. A. M. Hind I, 1915, p. 22, no. 31, Benesch IV, no. 736, fig. 882.   [³] 'Copy after an unknown original of about 1641–2 which seems to have been a companion piece to no. 735. Like the latter, also the original of the present drawing was signed. The signature has been copied by the draughtsman as well.'

75. School of Rembrandt, *Elegant couple* p. 199

DATA: Pen and bistre, on white paper 167 x 124 mm.

LITERATURE: Valentiner, no. 776*; Hirschmann, p. 17*. Von Seidlitz, p. 254, no. L41; Becker, *Neue Folge,* no. 26*. Catton Rich, p. 1, fig. 3*; Rosenberg 1964, p. 254, fig. 217*.

EXHIBITIONS: Amsterdam 1913, no. 79; Leiden 1916B, no. 41; Paris 1921, no. 63; The Hague 1930, I no. 92; Groningen 1931, no. 93; Groningen 1948, no. 11.

PROVENANCE: Art dealer A. Löbl, Paris 1913; — Collection Hofstede de Groot, inv. no. 517, bequest 1914, no. 100; — Groninger Museum voor Stad en Lande, inv. no. 1931–192.

The present drawing probably depicts two actors, a popular theme in Rembrandt's circle. Yet we do not believe that the drawing was made as early as the Actor in the character of

Pantalone (no. 56) when most of the authentic Rembrandt drawings of this subject were made. The present study may have been executed by a pupil, in the style of Rembrandt's drawings of 1648[1], a supposition that seems to be confirmed by another, exactly similar version of the drawing by the same hand, in Vienna.[2] Rosenberg (see Bibliography) compares our drawing to Marcantonio's engraving after Dürer[3], The promenade. Catton Rich (see Bibliography) reproduces the drawing together with a number of other representations of the iconographical theme of the promenade tradition.

[1] See Benesch III, no. 599, fig. 730; no. 603, fig. 734 and no. 606, fig. 737. [2] Akademie für bildenden Künste, inv. no. 3012 (see fig. 26). [3] Reproduced in Rosenberg 1964, fig. 216. Bartsch 94.

Fig. 26. School of Rembrandt, *Elegant couple*. Drawing, Vienna,
Akademie für bildenden Künste

76. School of Rembrandt, *Daniel in the lion's den* p. 200

DATA: Pen and bistre, bistre wash, on white paper 173 x 182 mm. Watermark no. 28.

LITERATURE: *Dessins de Rembrandt* 1909, no. 23*. Valentiner, no. 209; Hirschmann, p. 17; Von Seidlitz 1917, p. 254, no. 184; Lippmann-HdG, 4th series II, no. 100*; Benesch V, no. 1021, fig. 1235.

EXHIBITIONS: Amsterdam 1913, no. 19; Leiden 1916B, no. 84; The Hague 1930, I no. 80; Groningen 1931, no. 85.

PROVENANCE: Art dealer Colnaghi, London 1902; — Art dealer Paul Mathey, Paris 1904; — Anonymous sale, Paris 6.5.1909, no. 113; — Collection Hofstede de Groot, inv. no. 348, bequest 1914, no. 88; — Groninger Museum voor Stad en Lande, inv. no. 1931–184.

According to Benesch, the present drawing is 'the maturest, simplest and most monumental version of a theme, repeatedly treated by Rembrandt in drawings.' Though we share Benesch' admiration for 'the plastic synthesis of the figures, particularly prominent in the lions to the right which recall carved animal figures in early architecture,' there is little indication pointing to the authorship of Rembrandt. As well as some imposing qualities the drawing shows considerable weaknesses. The drawing of the head and body of Daniel, and of the tail of the standing lion is clumsily executed. One could cite as supporting proof of Rembrandt's authorship the fact that the typical way in which the figure is sitting can also be found in other drawings.[1] As these drawings, however, are not documented and merely attributed by Benesch to the master, one can only conclude that the drawing could have been made in Rembrandt's circle. We prefer to follow Professor Van de Waal's opinion, i.e. a copy after a lost original by Rembrandt.

[1] Rebekka and Eliezer, coll. Marignane, Paris, Benesch III, no. 566, fig. 696. Satan showing Christ the Kingdoms of the world, Berlin, Kupferstichkabinett, inv. no. 5281, Benesch III, no. 635, fig. 770. Adam and Eve, Philadelphia (Penn.), coll. David H. H. Felix, Benesch I, no. 163, fig. 173.

77. School of Rembrandt, *Study of a standing male nude*   p. 201

DATA: Pen and bistre, bistre wash, on brownish paper 229 x 128 mm. Watermark no. 29.
LITERATURE: Hofstede de Groot 1906, no. 2; Teding van Berkhout, no. 18*; Von Seidlitz, p. 254, no. 162.
EXHIBITIONS: Amsterdam 1913, no. 64; Groningen 1915, no. 50; Leiden 1916B, no. 62; Paris 1921, no. 66; The Hague 1930, I no. 81; Groningen 1931, no. 86; Groningen 1952, no. 73; The Hague 1955, no. 43.
PROVENANCE: Sale Boreel a.o., Amsterdam 15.6.1908, no. 486*; — Art dealer Colnaghi, London 1910; — Collection Hofstede de Groot, inv. no. 350, bequest 1914, no. 89; — Groninger Museum voor Stad en Lande, inv. no. 1931–185.

Among the large number of similar studies from the school of Rembrandt, Benesch only accepts a few[1] as being by Rembrandt himself. Some others[2] are included as attributions. Notwithstanding the rather good quality of our drawing, there is little doubt that it has been executed by a pupil. The knee-joints are indicated from the outside, whereas generally Rembrandt suggests the joints from the inside, as it were, almost effortlessly.

[1] Benesch IV, no. 709, fig. 852; no. 710, fig. 853; no. 710a, fig. 851; no. 711, fig. 854. [2] Benesch IV, no. A48, fig. 1061; no. A55, fig. 1060.

78. School of Rembrandt, *Scholar in a room, his right hand resting on a skull*   p. 202

DATA: Pen and bistre, on brownish paper 217 x 198 mm.
LITERATURE: Becker, no. 27*; Van de Waal, p. 47.
EXHIBITIONS: The Hague 1930, I no. 104; Groningen 1931, no. 105; Groningen 1948, no. 110; The Hague 1955, no. 15; Leiden 1956, no. 91.
PROVENANCE: Sale Daulby, Liverpool 12.8.1799, lot no. 87 (L. 5964); Art dealer Parsons, London 1920; — Collection Hofstede de Groot, inv. no. 663, bequest 1926; — Groninger Museum voor Stad en Lande, inv. no. 1931–204.

With slight variations this theme was assiduously treated over and again throughout the flowering of Rembrandt and his school. In Prof. Van de Waal's definitive treatise (see Bibliography) on Rembrandt's Faust etching, a list of a number of these representations is given. A direct prototype of the conception formed by Rembrandt and his school cannot be indicated because of the unique spiritual conditions which favoured the existence of this particular treatment of the theme. As Prof. Van de Waal points out, however, the archetype is the 'Hieronymus im Gehäuse'; the 'writing saints such as St. Jerome, St. Matthew, St. Gregory and St. Ambrosius' also contributed to the forming of the type. In Rembrandt's circle two aspects of the representation were stressed in particular. The Vanitas still-life and the genre element were becoming the main components. The attributes of learning and wisdom, old books, the globe and a skull are far away from the cool and sober instruments of truth with which a humanistic age liked to depict Hieronymus. Their emotional content has changed; they are symbolizing rather the ancient, almost witch-like wisdom of the pondering scholar. Like any romanticism, the particular brand in which Rembrandt and his followers were indulging was kept alive by a yearning for things that are far away, either in distance or in time. In the young, rationalistic and rigid society that Calvinism and commerce had created, the presence of the wise men of the Chosen People must have been a welcome and curious diversion. The newly established interpretation of the Faust etching shows that emotionally the subject could be connected with one of the most persecuted religious groups, that of the Socinians. As the present drawing is merely an uninteresting repetition of the theme, it would be a mistake to attribute too much thinking to it. We do not exaggerate, however, in saying that the frequent occurrence of the theme, with an emotional content as shown above, is easily understandable in a society that gave evidence of its discomfort towards Calvinist intolerance through of a multitude of sects.

The old tradition[1] of the authorship has been corrected in that Rembrandt's name is no longer connected with the drawing. The catalogues of the two exhibitions[2] in which Bol's name is mentioned as the artist, however, do not offer any evidence in support. Perhaps an etching by Bol[3] was the reason for this attribution. As we did not find sufficient comparable material, we prefer to catalogue the drawing as 'school of Rembrandt'.

[1] In the Daulby sale the drawing was sold as a Rembrandt.   [2] The Hague 1955 and Leiden 1956.   [3] Bartsch 8.

79. School of Rembrandt, *Oriental descending a hill towards a city*   p. 203

DATA: Pen and bistre, on white paper 202 x 277 mm. Owner's mark Esdaile (Lugt 2617), owner's mark Lawrence (Lugt 2445). Watermark no. 30.

LITERATURE: Valentiner, no. 127*; Becker, no. 39*; Hell, p. 105; Rotermund, p. 91, no. 76*.

EXHIBITIONS: The Hague 1930, I no. 97; Groningen 1931, no. 97.

PROVENANCE: Coll. Sir Thomas Lawrence; Collection William Esdaile; Art dealer Maggs Bros., London 1921; — Collection Hofstede de Groot, inv. no. 689, bequest 1926; — Groninger Museum voor Stad en Lande, inv. no. 1931–196.

Valentiner (see Bibliography) includes the drawing in his corpus as probably authentic; at least the composition is 'eine ausserordentliche Schöpfung der Spätzeit'. Indeed the drawing shows a remarkably visionary conception of space but we prefer to consider this as 'borrowed greatness', to use Mr. Lugt's aptly phrased judgement. The drawing must be related to a composition of the late fifties. The theme of the drawing has always been a mystery. Rotermund (see Bibliography) gives it the title 'Mose auf dem Berge Nebo' (5 Moses 34:1–4) '… er schaut in die Zukunft. Noch ist Jerusalem nicht zur heiligen Stadt erhöht. Er aber darf sie schauen, mit ihren Mauern und Zinnen, mit der Kuppel des Tempels.' Against this designation, however, stands the fact that Moses is generally depicted with his staff. Prof. Van de Waal suggested that the prophet Jonah may be represented here, looking down on the city of Ninivéh.

80. School of Rembrandt (Gerbrand van den Eeckhout?), *Elisha fed by the ravens* p. 204

DATA: Pen and bistre, bistre wash, on white paper 208 x 280 mm.

LITERATURE: Valentiner, no.184*; Becker, *Neue Folge,* no. 30*; Hell, p. 105, note no. 2; Schinnerer, p. 34, no. 85*; Rotermund, p. 103, no. 121*.

EXHIBITIONS: Paris 1921, no. 53; The Hague 1930, I no. 99; Groningen 1931, no. 99.

PROVENANCE: Art dealer Parsons, London 1919; — Collection Hofstede de Groot, inv. no. 624, bequest 1926; — Groninger Museum voor Stad en Lande, inv. no. 1931–198.

Like the preceding drawing, the present one has an imposing eloquence which, in this instance, goes beyond merely a good composition. Not only does the figure speak a powerful language[1] but also the landscape seems to implement the action. The execution is a more complicated matter than merely 'auffällig schwach'[2]; it is a curious mixture of careless swiftness and at the same time effective drawing. Little hesitation is felt here, contrary to the preceding number. If we compare the drawing with similar sketches from Benesch's Rembrandt-corpus, we fail to see why our drawing has not been included in the little group of Vol. V, nos. 900–912. In particular a drawing in Paris,[3] Tobias and the angel at the river, must originate from the same hand. Concerning the latter drawing, Benesch mentions 'A painting by a pupil, based on the present drawing.'[4] Recalling Dr. Sumowski's words in his article on Eeckhout drawings,[5] we are inclined to consider the drawing as an authentic composition of one of the later years, possibly by Gerbrand van den Eeckhout, as there are several comparable drawings[6] attributed to this artist.

[1] Schinnerer (see Bibliography): 'Die Figur, im Bau ganz auf die Bewegung der flehenden Hände gestellt, könnte nicht Rembrandtischer sein. Wie spricht der leere Raum mit den Raben!' Rotermund (see Bibliography): '… ein sich Ausstrecken, der nahenden Hilfe entgegen.' [2] Valentiner, no. 184. [3] Louvre, L. Bonnat Bequest. Lugt, III, no. 1122, Hofstede de Groot 1906, no. 679, Benesch V, no. 908*. [4] Berlin, Kaiser Friedrich Museum, W. Bode, Jahrbuch der Preussischen Kunstsammlungen 31, 1910, pp. 159–163. See also W. R. Valentiner, *Rembrandt, wiedergefundene Gemälde,* 1923, p. 67. [5] W. Sumowski, 'Gerbrand van den Eeckhout als Zeichner', in *Oud Holland* LXXVII, 1962, 1, p. 29: 'Da die Schüler während der Lehrzeit auf engen künstlerischen Anschluss an den Meister aus waren, müssen sie auch im Stile Rembrandts gezeichnet haben. Die Zuschreibung derartiger Blätter ist besonders schwierig weil diese Nachahmungsbestrebungen zum Verzicht auf individuelle Eigenheiten führten. Je nach dem Grade der erreichten Annäherung wird das entsprechende Material im Bestande der Rembrandt oder der anonymen Schule gegebenen Arbeiten aufgegangen sein. Meines Erachtens darf man nachweisbare Entwürfe für Gemälde den betreffenden Schülern zurückgeben, auch wenn der Stil solcher Blätter nicht ohne weiteres mit den gesicherten Zeichenweisen der einzelnen Persönlichkeiten vereinbar ist. Die Gemälde setzen der Forscher in die Lage, gleichsam verschollene Stilformen

der Schüler als Zeichner zu entdecken. Ich vermute, dass die Rembrandtnachfolger nicht nur in ihrer individuellen Art, sondern gleichzeitig auch in der Manier ihrer Lehrers gezeichnet haben.' [⁶] See Titus Manlius,
drawing attributed to Gerbrand van den Eeckhout, Rotterdam, Museum Boymans-van Beuningen, repr. in
Oud Holland LXXXII, 1962, 1, Pl. 50; Judas in despair, attributed to Eeckhout, coll. S. de Clerq, The Hague (Photograph Rijksbureau voor Kunsthistorische Documentatie, The Hague).

81. School of Rembrandt, *Christ among the doctors* p. 205

DATA: Pen and various kinds of bistre, bistre wash, on white paper 161 x 239 mm.

LITERATURE: Benesch VI, no. A87, fig. 1656; Sumowski, p. 27, no. A87.

EXHIBITIONS: The Hague 1930, I no. 102; Groningen 1931, no. 102; Groningen 1952, no. 77; Amsterdam 1964, no. 96.

PROVENANCE: Collection Nebehay, Vienna 1926; — Collection Hofstede de Groot, inv. no. 950,
bequest 1926; — Groninger Museum voor Stad en Lande, inv. no. 1931–201.

Benesch indicates a large group of drawings to which the present one belongs. The author of
this group is not known and on this occasion has been 'seemingly inspired by the composition
of the etching of 1652, Bartsch 65, Hind 257'.[1] Werner Sumowski mentions[2] a copy after our
drawing in Munich.[3] The man in the background holding the staff of office may have been
taken from a painting of a circumcision by Rembrandt in 1646 for Prince Frederik Hendrik.[4]

[1] Benesch VI, no. A87, fig. 1656. [2] See Bibliography Sumowski, p. 27, no. A87. [3] Graphische Sammlung,
inv. no. 1419, Hofstede de Groot 1906, no. 381. [4] Now lost. A copy in the Museum, Brunswick, cat. 1910, no. 241.

82. School of Rembrandt, *The Shunamite woman before Elisha at Mount Carmel* p. 206

DATA: Pen and bistre, on brownish paper 177 x 200 mm. Recto, lower right corner: owner's
mark J. Richardson Sr. (Lugt 2183). On the mount: owner's mark Barnard (Lugt 1419). Verso:
'J:B N: 666- 8 by 7' (Lugt 1420), owner's mark Th. Miller Whitehead (Lugt 2449) and '1856'.
Pasted on paper, no visible watermark.

LITERATURE: Valentiner, no. 192*; Becker, *Neue Folge,* no. 33*; Teding van Berkhout, no. 6*;
Von Seidlitz, p. 254, no. L76; Hirschmann, p. 18.

EXHIBITIONS: Amsterdam 1913, no. 15; Groningen 1915, no. 49; Leiden 1916B, no. 76; The Hague
1930, I no. 79; Groningen 1931, no. 84; Groningen 1948, no. 99.

PROVENANCE: Coll. John Richardson Sr.; Coll. John Barnard; Coll. Th. Miller Whitehead;
Art dealer Obach, London 1905; — Collection Hofstede de Groot, inv. no. 347, bequest 1914,
no. 87; — Groninger Museum voor Stad en Lande, inv. no. 1931–183.

There is general agreement concerning the present drawing. It is a typical product of a pupil,
not necessarily based on a specific drawing by Rembrandt, but in the style of the later years.

83. Imitator of Rembrandt, *A family in a large interior*   p. 207

DATA: Pen and bistre, bistre wash, on white paper 167 x 234 mm. Glued on paper, no visible watermark.

LITERATURE: Poortenaar, no. 30.

EXHIBITIONS: The Hague 1930, I no. 101; Groningen 1931, no. 101; Groningen 1948, no. 109.

PROVENANCE: Sale Klinkosch, Vienna 15.4.1889, no. 746 (L. 48170); Sale Brownlow, London 14.7.1926, no. 50; — Art dealer Parsons, London mag. cat. no. 45, 1926, no. 482; — Collection Hofstede de Groot, inv. no. 974, bequest 1926; — Groninger Museum voor Stad en Lande, inv. no. 1931–200.

There are several elements in the present drawing that point to its being at least a copy. The constructional impossibility of the window, an anachronism in itself, the affected cosiness of the scene, and the emphasis laid on 'period' in the room indicate that the drawing bears no relation to Rembrandt or even to his school. Although the paper appears to be old, we may have here an imitation of the late eighteenth or nineteenth century.

Figs. 27, 28. Imitator of Rembrandt, *Landscapes with a river and cottages*. Drawings, Haarlem, Teylers Museum

84. Imitator of Rembrandt, *Landscape with a farmhouse and a draughtsman* p. 208

DATA: Pen and bistre, brown wash, on white paper 85 x 135 mm. Verso: owner's mark Heseltine (Lugt 1507), owner's mark Robinson (Lugt 2141b) and '1891'.

LITERATURE: Hofstede de Groot 1906, no. IIII; Teding van Berkhout, no. 23*; Hirschmann, p. 20-21; Von Seidlitz, p. 254, no. L52; Van Regteren Altena 1931, p. 71; Benesch 1935, p. 47; H. E. van Gelder, no. 41b*; Benesch VI, 1340, fig. 1574.

EXHIBITIONS: London 1899, no. 109; Amsterdam 1913, no. 87; Leiden 1916B, no. 80; The Hague 1930, I no. 88; Groningen 1931, no. 109; Groningen 1948, no. 101; Groningen 1952, no. 71; The Hague 1955, no. 46.

PROVENANCE: Coll. Robinson; Coll. Heseltine, London, cat. 1907, no. 75; — Art dealer Colnaghi, London 1913; — Collection Hofstede de Groot, inv. no. 513, bequest 1914, no. 96; — Groninger Museum voor Stad en Lande, inv. no. 1931-208.

In considering the present drawing, we are confronted with several incongruous facts. In the first place it is not easy to understand why the writers mentioned in the bibliography accepted the drawing as a Rembrandt. Then, in Teyler's Museum at Haarlem, there are two drawings,[1] obviously by the same hand and unmistakeably very weak copies from the last half of the eighteenth century. If, consequently, we assume that our drawing is executed by the same artist, it remains to be explained why nobody ever felt the necessity of accepting these two drawings in Haarlem also as Rembrandts. The four landscapes with which Benesch compares our drawing only serve to show that the forger took this type of Rembrandt's drawings as his model.

[1] Inv. nos. Q*71 and 72. The paper of these drawings, like that of the one in Groningen, seems to point to the eighteenth century. See figs. 27 and 28.

85. Roeland Roghman, *The Pierre-Pertuis pass* p. 209

DATA: Black chalk, pen and bistre, bistre and brown wash, on white paper 152 x 231 mm. Recto, lower right side, signed 'R. Roghman'. Watermark Foolscap.

LITERATURE: Hirschmann, p. 204.

EXHIBITIONS: Leiden 1916C, no. 80; The Hague 1930, I no. 112; Groningen 1931, no. 116; Groningen 1952, no. 78.

PROVENANCE: Sale Esdaile, London (Christie) 18.6.1840, no. 704? (L. 15865); Sale H. Duval, Amsterdam 22.6.1910, no. 314; — Collection Hofstede de Groot, inv. no. 428, bequest 1914, no. 52. — Groninger Museum voor Stad en Lande, inv. no. 1931-215.

A number of drawings of the same pass by other artists[1] exist. Our drawing, however, needs not necessarily be considered as dependant on these other representations of the theme because the artist used to travel a good deal. Also the motif of a gateway through a rock was a favorite one with Roghman: in at least five other drawings[2] a similar motif can be seen.

The present drawing is a good example of an interesting part of Roghman's oeuvre. The importance of this group of drawings lies in its intriguing atmosphere, which is unique of its kind. Though there is a distinct affinity with the work of Rembrandt, Doomer, De Vlieger and Waterloo, the artist is capable of suggesting his own world in a persuasive manner, revealing an almost passionate romanticism. For Dutch artists of the middle decades of the century, landscape satisfied the need for expressive media; Roghman appears to have adopted this tradition, contributing his rich visionary power to it.

[1] Vincent Laurensz. van der Vinne, Haarlem, Municipal Archives, dated 1653. Lambert Doomer, Leiden, Printroom of the University, inv. no. AW 207. Herman Saftleven, Berlin, Kupferstichkabinett, cat. Bock/Rosenberg, 1930, no. 13848. Jan Hackaert, Zürich, Kunsthaus, Album Hackaert. A. Waterloo, The British Museum, cat. A. M. Hind, Vol. IV, 1931, p. 104, no. 10. See also: Stelling-Michaud, *Unbekannte Schweizerische Landschaften,* Zürich/Leipzig, 1937, p. 52. [2] München, Staatliche Graphische Sammlung, inv. no. 1346. London, Victoria & Albert Museum, Dyce Bequest no. 456, cat. 1921, no. 118*. London, coll. Sir Robert Witt, Hand-list 1956, p. 112, no. 3438. Paris, coll. F. Lugt, inv. no. 6693, Bernt II, no. 497. Dresden, Kupferstichkabinett (photograph Rijksbureau voor Kunsthistorische Documentatie, The Hague), inv. no. C1770, 158 x 235 mm.

86. Roeland Roghman, *Landscape with a chapel, a fortified bridge, and a perspective with mountains* p. 210

DATA: Black chalk, pen and bistre, bistre and grey wash, on white paper; 155 x 230 mm. Recto, lower right side, brush and brown ink: 'R Roghman', owner's mark Gigoux (Lugt 1164). Watermark: Foolscap.

LITERATURE: Hirschmann, p. 204.

EXHIBITIONS: The Hague 1902, no. 80; Leiden 1916C, no. 81; The Hague 1930, I no. 110; Groningen 1931, no. 114.

PROVENANCE: Sale Gigoux, Paris 20.3.1882, no. 424 (L. 41800); Art dealer Van Gogh, Amsterdam 1901; — Collection Hofstede de Groot, inv. no. 100, bequest 1914, no. 50; — Groninger Museum voor Stad en Lande, inv. no. 1931–213.

Like the preceding number, this is a drawing in Roghman's characteristic style with a faded but certainly genuine signature. Art dealer Van Gogh bought the drawing at the Gigoux-sale in 1882, together with no. 88.

87. Roeland Roghman, *View of the village of Rijnsburg* p. 211

DATA: Black chalk, grey wash, on white paper 140 x 200 mm. Recto, in the middle foreground, in black chalk: 'vliet' or 'vlas'.

EXHIBITIONS: The Hague 1902, no. 81; Leiden 1916A, no. 78; The Hague 1930, I no. 109; Groningen 1931, no. 113; The Hague 1955, no. 47.

PROVENANCE: Art dealer Van Gogh, Amsterdam 1901; — Collection Hofstede de Groot, inv. no. 99, bequest 1914, no. 49; — Groninger Museum voor Stad en Lande, inv. no. 1931–212.

Our drawing was used as a model for the engraving by Rademaker.[1] Print and drawing are in the same direction, so Rademaker probably first drew a reduced and reverse copy from which he made the engraving. In the *Kabinet* there are three illustrations of the village of Rijnsburg, apparently belonging together, so the two other drawings may still be in existence, possibly

97. Cornelis Troost?, *Study of a seated gentleman*

under another name, as our drawing is not so typical of Roghman's style as the preceding two numbers. In his preface to the *Kabinet* Rademaker says '.. We made use of the Draughts of the greatest Masters of Old, that we could find in the Cabinets of the virtuosus, and because those Draughts were of no use but to the possessors of them, we got them to be engraved, to Impart them to the Publick ...'

We did not succeed in finding another provenance, so that we are not able to check the attribution in this way. There are, however, two drawings, also attributed to Roghman, that show the same hand. In the Rijksprentenkabinet at Amsterdam[2] there is a view of Heukelom; a landscape with a country-road was, in 1942, in the possession of art dealer Mellaert, The Hague.

[1] Abraham Rademaker, *Kabinet van Nederlandsche Outheden en Gezichten*, Amsterdam, 1725, Vol. I, Pl. 76.   [2] Inv. no. A4532.

88. Roeland Roghman, *The river Amstel near Ouderkerk*   p. 212

DATA: Brush-drawing in grey, on white paper 123 x 223 mm. Recto: owner's mark Gigoux (Lugt 1164). Verso: impress of the copying-needle; inscribed 'N 3544' (Lugt 2987). Watermark no. 31.

LITERATURE: Lugt 1920, p. 121; Brugmans III, p. 254*.

EXHIBITIONS: Leiden 1916C, no. 79; The Hague 1930, I no. 111; Groningen 1931, no. 115; The Hague 1955, no. 48.

PROVENANCE: Sale Hulswit, Amsterdam 20.10.1822, Kbk H, no. 27 (L. 10327); — Sale Goll van Franckenstein, Amsterdam 1.7.1833, Kbk KK, no. 52 (L. 13362); — Sale Woodburn, London 16.6.1854, no. 1683 (L. 21988); Sale Gigoux, Paris 20.3.1882, no. 427 (L. 41800); — Art dealer Van Gogh, Amsterdam 1908; — Collection Hofstede de Groot, inv. no. 427, bequest 1914, no. 51; — Groninger Museum voor Stad en Lande, inv. no. 1931–214.

The scene of the present drawing was engraved as one of a series of six prints,[1] representing the six villages upon which the militia of Prince William II was quartered during the siege of Amsterdam in the summer of 1650. The drawing has in verso the impress of a copying needle, just like a drawing of the same measurements and technique in Haarlem,[2] the likeness of which we also find on one of the prints.

Fig. 29. Roeland Roghman, *The village of Amstelveen*. Drawing, Haarlem, Teylers Museum

It is not known after which artist and by whom the prints were made. Muller (see note 1) changes his attribution from Geertrui to Roeland Roghman without giving any reason. As the impress of the copying-needle is on the back of the drawings, it is equally possible that we are dealing with models for the prints, or with copies made from them. As Roghman's work shows a wide variety of techniques ranging from the restrained and exact representations of the castles of the Netherlands to his romantic and free drawing of mountain landscapes, the drawings could be classed within his oeuvre without much trouble. The relatively good quality is also in favour of Roghman's authorship.

[1] The print is in the same direction as the drawing. See F. Muller, *Beredeneerde beschrijving van Nederlandsche historieplaten*, etc., I, Amsterdam, 1863-70, no. 2007; IV, Amsterdam, 1882, no. 2007. [2] The village of Amstelveen, Teylers Museum, Cat. no. O*54. See also Lugt 1920, p. 101 ff., where a detailed account of the events is given. See fig. 29.

89. Jacob van Ruisdael, *The ruins of the castle of Egmond* p. 213

DATA: Black chalk, grey wash, on white paper 201 x 285 mm. Signed in the lower right corner with monogram 'JvR'. Recto, upper left corner, in black chalk: 'Egmont op d hoef', upper right corner: owner's mark Robinson (Lugt 1433). Verso: owner's mark Heseltine (Lugt 1507). Watermark no. 32.

LITERATURE: De Vries Lam*; Hirschmann, p. 210; Becker, no. 44*; Rosenberg 1928, p. 113, no. z25; Simon, p. 85; Frerichs 1963, p. 52, no. 66.

EXHIBITIONS: Leiden 1916C, no. 83; The Hague 1930, I no. 114; Groningen 1931, no. 118; Groningen 1952, no. 80; Vancouver 1958, no. 66*; Brussels 1961, no. 123.

PROVENANCE: Sale Feitama, Amsterdam 16.10.1758, Kbk H, no. 44 or 45 (L. 1019); — Collection Th. Lawrence; — Collection S. Woodburn; Collection J. C. Robinson; Sale Heseltine, Amsterdam 27.5.1913, no. 189*; — Collection Hofstede de Groot, inv. no. 527, bequest 1914, no. 54; — Groninger Museum voor Stad en Lande, inv. no. 1931-217.

Judging by the number of drawings and paintings representing these ruins, Ruisdael must have worked often at this place that was so well suited to his taste for the heroic aspect of nature. Several of these drawings have a similar monogram and the same measurements.[1]

Strangely enough, Hofstede de Groot and Simon have expressed some doubts about the authorship of Ruisdael. Rosenberg writes that De Groot attributed this drawing to Dirk Dalens, but he did not agree with this opinion. According to Lugt, the clouds may have been added afterwards. As Woodburn's collection contained many drawings from the Goll van Franckenstein sale, the supposition[2] that Josi saw our drawing together with the two in Amsterdam in Goll's collection seems probable.

[1] Rosenberg 1928, nos. 13 and 14, sale Huldschinsky, Berlin 3.11.1931, nos. 76 and 77, 200 x 285 mm and 204 x 285 mm. Rosenberg 1928, nos. 2 and 3, Amsterdam, Printroom of the Rijksmuseum, inv. nos. A4560 and A4561, 196 x 298 mm and 197 x 303 mm (no A4560 likewise inscribed: 'Egmond op d hoef'). [2] Miss Frerichs's catalogue (see Bibliography Frerichs 1963) reports an entry in C. Josi, *Collection d'imitations de dessins d'après les principaux maîtres hollandais et flamands* etc., London 1821, saying that Josi knew three drawings representing the ruins of Egmond in the Goll collection. Only two of these, however, are mentioned in the catalogue of the Goll sale (Kbk N, no. 7).

90. Jacob van Ruisdael?, *Landscape with sheds on the bank of a canal*   p. 214

DATA: Black chalk, grey wash, on white paper 164 x 248 mm. Verso: owner's mark R. von Liphart (Lugt 1758) and '934', owner's mark K. E. von Liphart (Lugt 1687). Watermark no. 33.

LITERATURE: Hirschmann, no. 210; Rosenberg 1928, no. 24; Simon, p. 85.

EXHIBITIONS: Leiden 1916C, no. 84; The Hague 1930, I no. 113; Groningen 1931, no. 117; Groningen 1948, no. 112; Groningen 1952, no. 79*.

PROVENANCE: Collection R. von Liphart; — Sale K. E. von Liphart, Leipzig 26.4.1898, no. 1035 (L. 56238); — Art dealer Frederik Muller, Amsterdam 1906; — Collection Hofstede de Groot, inv. no. 313, bequest 1914, no. 53; — Groninger Museum voor Stad en Lande, inv. no. 1931–216.

Rosenberg accepted the drawing as a work by Ruisdael, but does not dwell upon any particular aspects. If we assume that the draughtsman was a follower of Ruisdael, we have to think of an artist capable of expressing himself with great visionary power.[1]

The scene of our drawing has not been identified exactly. We may assume, however, that the dunes and mills of this landscape are to be found near Beverwijk or IJmuiden, not far from Haarlem. A drawing exists by Ruisdael,[2] inscribed 'Velsen' (also in this neighbourhood), that shows the same rough and incoherent drawing as in the present landscape. A similar scene can be seen in Philips Koninck's drawing of the mills of the Bleekerspad near Amsterdam.[3]

[1] At the Von Liphart sale the drawing was catalogued as Anthonie Waterloo.   [2] Amsterdam, Rijksprentenkabinet, inv. no. A3485, Rosenberg 1928, no. 21.   [3] Coll. Bernard Houthakker, exh. Amsterdam 1964, no. 44, Gerson 1936, no. 23*.

91. Cornelis Saftleven, *Woman, sitting near a kitchen fire*   p. 215

DATA: Black chalk, on white paper 275 x 207 mm. Recto, lower left side, in black chalk: 'CS 1656'. Watermark no. 34.

LITERATURE: Henkel 1916, p. 341; Hirschmann, p. 408; Becker, *Neue Folge*, no. 36*.

EXHIBITIONS: Leiden 1916A, no. 79; The Hague 1930, I no. 115; Groningen 1931, no. 119; Groningen 1952, no. 81.

PROVENANCE: Sale Duval, Amsterdam 22.6.1910, no. 345; — Collection Hofstede de Groot, inv. no. 433, bequest 1914, no. 55; — Groninger Museum voor Stad en Lande, inv. no. 1931–218.

This good, well-preserved drawing is comparable in style as well as in subject-matter with the oeuvre of Cornelis Saftleven. Not only do we have confidence in the monogram and date, but also the quality of the drawing, especially for instance of the large jar to the left, is in keeping with Saftleven's ability as a draughtsman, a fine example of which is to be seen for instance in a drawing of a roebuck, in the collection of Sir Bruce Ingram, Fitzwilliam Museum, Cambridge, exhibited Rotterdam 1961, no. 76*.

92. Cornelis Saftleven, *Standing youth in a long coat*   p. 216

DATA: Black and white chalk, on brownish paper 304 x 194 mm. Recto, lower right side, in black chalk: 'CS 1657'. Watermark no. 35.

LITERATURE: Hirschmann, p. 408.
EXHIBITIONS: Leiden 1916A, no. 80; The Hague 1930, I no. 117; Groningen 1931, no. 120; Groningen 1952, no. 82; The Hague 1955, no. 49.
PROVENANCE: Sale Van Gogh, Amsterdam 2.12.1913, no. 679; — Collection Hofstede de Groot. inv. no. 539, bequest 1914, no. 56; — Groninger Museum voor Stad en Lande, inv. no. 1931–219.

There is no doubt as to Saftleven's authorship because the drawing is characteristic of a large group of figure studies by the artist, which are to be found in almost any of the important collections. A great number of Saftleven's drawings bear a date. Through these dates it is apparent that Saftleven's style has not changed significantly in the course of several decades.

93. Cornelis Saftleven?, *Sleeping boy* p. 217

DATA: Black chalk, traces of body-white, on brownish paper 182 x 151 mm. Recto, in black chalk, to the left: 'CS 1659'. Watermark no. 36.
LITERATURE: Henkel 1916, p. 341; Hirschmann, p. 408.
EXHIBITIONS: Leiden 1916A, no. 81; The Hague 1930, I no. 116; Groningen 1931, no. 121.
PROVENANCE: Sale Van Gogh, Amsterdam 2.12.1913, no. 680; — Collection Hofstede de Groot, inv. no. 540, bequest 1914, no. 57; — Groninger Museum voor Stad en Lande, inv. no. 1931–220.

Although this drawing is entirely in the manner of Saftleven's figure-studies, it may have been retouched heavily. Also there are several weaknesses in the drawing, in particular the inefficiently executed foreshortening and the drawing of the hand and the face.

94. Herman Saftleven, *A dingy at a ship-yard* p. 218

DATA: Black chalk, bistre wash, on white paper 147 x 278 mm. Verso: owner's mark De Vos (Lugt 1450). Watermark Coat of arms (too indistinct for reproduction).
LITERATURE: Henkel 1916, p. 342; Hirschmann, p. 408.
EXHIBITIONS: Leiden 1916A, no. 84; The Hague 1930, I no. 118; Groningen 1931, no. 122; Groningen 1952, no. 86*.
PROVENANCE: Sale De Vos, Amsterdam 22.5.1883, no. 695? (L. 43060); Art dealer Van Gogh, Amsterdam, Magazine catalogue I, 1908, no. 58; — Collection Hofstede de Groot, inv. no. 434, bequest 1914, no. 58; — Groninger Museum voor Stad en Lande, inv. no. 1931–221.

The attribution to Herman Saftleven seems to be correct. The subject of the scene is not incompatible with Saftleven's predilection for river-landscapes with boats and ship-yards. Also the sheet is a very good example of his fresh style of drawing. A copy or engraving may have been made after the drawing, as the paper is pierced with the needle. We have not found, however, any such copy or engraving. The drawing may have been made in Saftleven's later Utrecht years.

95. Herman Saftleven, *Composition with topographical elements of the city of Prague*

p. 219

DATA: Black chalk, pen and black ink, grey wash, on white paper 348 x 382 mm.

LITERATURE: Henkel 1916, p. 337; Hirschmann, p. 403; Van Regteren Altena 1931, p. 72*.

EXHIBITIONS: Leiden 1916A, no. 95; The Hague 1930, I no. 124; Groningen 1931, no. 128; Groningen 1952, no. 87; The Hague 1955, no. 53.

PROVENANCE: Art dealer Strölin, Paris 1906; — Collection Hofstede de Groot, inv. no. 304, bequest 1914, no. 62; — Groninger Museum voor Stad en Lande, inv. no. 1931–227.

Fig. 30. Herman Saftleven, *Draughtsman, sketching an old house*. Drawing, Frankfurt a.M., Städelsches Kunstinstitut

The drawing has alternatively been ascribed to Roeland Savery and Esaias van de Velde. Probably the way in which the man riding on horseback in the middle plane has been drawn was the reason for the latter attribution. Roeland Savery's name has understandably been brought up in connection with his many vistas of Prague, where he worked in the service of the Emperor Rudolf II. Yet we do not think that either of the two attributions is correct, as the quality of the drawing leaves much to be desired. The turrets and houses in the middle plane must have been executed by a very weak or inexperienced hand. Also it is hard to imagine that Savery, who knew Prague so well, could have made a drawing in which several topographic imperfections can be noted.[1] Mr. Frits Lugt and Miss Frerichs proposed the attribution to Herman Saftleven. Two other drawings, one in the Städelsches Kunstinstitut at Frankfurt a.M.[2], the other in the Hessisches Landesmuseum at Darmstadt[3], both with the monogram of Herman Saftleven, confirm this supposition. Specially the drawing in Frankfurt shows a striking similarity with our drawing (see fig. 30).

Living in Utrecht from the year 1634, Saftleven had been the pupil of Roeland Savery who died at Utrecht in 1639. It would not be unnatural to assume that Saftleven practised his hand in the manner of Savery's topographical drawings and that, in doing so, he used elements of the views of the city of Prague. We can account for the reminders of Esaias van de Velde's work when we bear in mind that Saftleven had only just left the atelier of Jan van Goyen, who in the years 1617–18 was deeply impressed by Esaias van de Velde.

[1] The fortified buildings to the left, in the distance, cannot be accurately identified. The Hradschin is actually situated much higher and thus does not directly verge upon the banks of the river Moldau.   [2] Inv. no. 938, Draughtsman, sketching an old house.   [3] Inv. no. 797, Landscape with travellers.

96. Michael Sweerts?, *Portrait of a boy* p. 220

DATA: Black and red chalk, on white paper 182 x 136 mm, the corners cut off. Recto, lower left corner: owner's mark De Valori (Lugt 2500), partly removed. Verso: unidentified owner's mark (Lugt 2870).

LITERATURE: Hirschmann, p. 209; Becker, *Neue Folge,* no. 37*; Van Regteren Altena 1931, p. 74; Stechow 1951, p. 212 and note 25.

EXHIBITIONS: Groningen 1915, no. 40; Leiden 1916C, no. 92; The Hague 1930, I no. 119; Groningen 1931, no. 123; The Hague 1955, no. 50.

PROVENANCE: Sale De Valori, Paris 26.11.1907, no. 236; — Collection Hofstede de Groot, inv. no. 321, bequest 1914, no. 59; — Groninger Museum voor Stad en Lande, inv. no. 1931–222.

At the Valori sale this portrait passed under the name of Gerard Terborch. The present attribution, viz. to Michael Sweerts, originates from Hofstede de Groot. According to the catalogue of the Groningen exhibition in 1931[1] the present portrait would represent the same boy as can be seen in a painting, also in the Hofstede de Groot bequest to Groningen. This resemblance, however, seems as questionable as the attribution itself.

[1] See the entry under no. 24; see also Bibliography Stechow 1951.

97. Cornelis Troost?, *Study of a seated gentleman* p. 113

DATA: Black, red and yellow chalk, on blue paper 265 x 205 mm.

LITERATURE: Hirschmann, p. 211; Van Regteren Altena 1931, p. 70*; Henkel 1939, p. 427.

EXHIBITIONS: Leiden 1916C, no. 96; The Hague 1930, I no. 120; Groningen 1931, no. 124; Groningen 1952, no. 88.

PROVENANCE: Art dealer Hoogendijk, Amsterdam; — Collection Hofstede de Groot, inv. no. 437, bequest 1914, no. 60; — Groninger Museum voor Stad en Lande, inv. no. 1931–223.

No painting or crayon-drawing by Troost, as far as we know, shows the exact figure from the present drawing, which has the appearance of being a preparatory sketch. With slight variations the figure can be found in two paintings,[1] attributed to Troost.

[1] Inequal love, Amsterdam, Collection Six (photograph Rijksbureau voor Kunsthistorische Documentatie); The guardroom, gouache, coll. P. Quaroni, London, ex. coll. John Howard, repr. in *Vier Generaties Nijstad,* Lochem/'s-Gravenhage 1962. As the pose, however, is commonplace in eighteenth century painting, we should not conclude too much from this comparison.

98. Wallerant Vaillant, *Portrait of Dr Jan Bicker* p. 221

DATA: Black and white chalk, black and white body-colour on greyish paper 370 x 347 mm, upper corners rounded off.

EXHIBITIONS: Leiden 1916C, no. 102; The Hague 1930, I no. 121; Groningen 1931, no. 126.

PROVENANCE: Unknown art dealer 1903; — Collection Hofstede de Groot, inv. no. 225, bequest 1914, no. 105; — Groninger Museum voor Stad en Lande, inv. no. 1931–225.

See text of the next entry.

99. Wallerant Vaillant, *Portrait of Jacob Bicker* p. 222

DATA: Black and white chalk, black and white body-colour, on greyish paper 407 x 355 mm. Signed in the upper right corner: 'W. Vaillant fecit 1648'.

EXHIBITIONS: Leiden 1916C, no. 101; The Hague 1930, I no. 122; Groningen 1931, no. 125.

PROVENANCE: Unknown art dealer 1903; — Collection Hofstede de Groot, inv. no. 224, bequest 1914, no. 104; — Groninger Museum voor Stad en Lande, inv. no. 1931–224.

Vaillant did many portraits of the Bicker and Alewijn families. Most of these portraits have been kept together, and were sold twice during this century in Amsterdam.[1] Hofstede de Groot bought the two drawings at the door in 1903, and it has not been possible to establish the provenance. The sitters have been identified[2] as Bickers by means of documented portraits, e.g. another pastel-drawing of Jacob Bicker by W. Vaillant, signed and dated 1651, sale Adama van Scheltema, no. 658, Pl. 67, 396 x 344 mm, and a painted portrait of Dr Jan Bicker by Joachim von Sandrart, dated 1639, now in the Rijksmuseum at Amsterdam, inv. no. 235.

[1] Sale Adama van Scheltema, Amsterdam (Frederik Muller) 11.6.1912 and sale Amsterdam (Mensing) 29.11.1939. [2] We are indebted to Jhr. J. L. F. O. van Kretschmar of the Iconografisch bureau in The Hague for his kind cooperation in this matter.

100. Adriaan van de Velde, *Herdsmen and cattle at a watering-place* p. 223

DATA: Brush-drawing, grey wash, on white paper 142 x 209 mm. Signed on the lower left side: 'AVV 1656'. Recto, upper right corner: owner's mark Habich (Lugt 862), lower left corner: owner's mark Mayor (Lugt 2799). Watermark no. 37.

LITERATURE: Hirschmann, p. 209.

EXHIBITIONS: Leiden 1916C, no. 107; The Hague 1930, I no. 123; Groningen 1931, no. 127.

PROVENANCE: Coll. William Mayor, London cat. 1875, no. 858, cat. 1871, no. 477; Sale E. Habich, Stuttgart 27.4.1899, no. 690 (L. 57164); — Sale F. A. v. S., Amsterdam 11.6.1912, no. 258; — Collection Hofstede de Groot, inv. no. 120, bequest 1914, no. 61; — Groninger Museum voor Stad en Lande, inv. no. 1931–226.

In the Habich collection at Kassel, our drawing had a companion piece of the same date and technique, also a signed landscape with cattle and herdsmen.[1] Drawings of Adriaan van de Velde were always present in the important old collections, doubtless because of their high quality. It strikes us therefore as curious that art historians have never lavished their favours upon the artist. Van de Velde's oeuvre has never been placed in its historical background. Yet it seems possible that this genre might be found to be closely linked with an important trend in Dutch literature, called the 'pastorale', of which Hooft's *Granida and Daifilo* is a well-known example.

[1] Reproduced in Eisenmann, no. 24.

101. Esaias van de Velde, *Landscape with gallows* p. 224

DATA: Black chalk, on white paper 201 x 305 mm. Signed at the foot: 'E V VELDE 1627'. Watermark no. 38.
LITERATURE: Hirschmann, p. 403; Van Regteren Altena 1931, p. 72.
EXHIBITIONS: Leiden 1916A, no. 93; The Hague 1930, I no. 125; Groningen 1931, no. 129; Groningen 1952, no. 89; The Hague 1955, no. 51; Prague 1966, no. 55.
PROVENANCE: Art dealer Strölin, Paris 1906; — Collection Hofstede de Groot, inv. no. 305, bequest 1914, no. 63; — Groninger Museum voor Stad en Lande, inv. no. 1931–228.

The collection contains two drawings from the year 1627 (see no. 28). A comparison may prove interesting, as there are instructive similarities and differences.

In 1627, Van Goyen had already left Van de Velde's atelier for several years. Both landscapes are executed in the short, somewhat dry drawing of the time. In several respects, however, Van Goyen's composition is more modern. The organization of the scene is directed towards the group of travellers. This leading idea is lacking in Esaias' conception. Here the horizon is placed higher, betraying the training of an earlier generation. His landscape is vaguely reminiscent of a bird's eye-view, whereas Van Goyen has placed himself within the landscape, reducing to profiles all the obstacles that the eye encounters.

Averkamp's ice-landscape (no. 1), which we placed around the year 1627, appears to represent yet another stage of development than Esaias' drawing. By means of isocephaly, Averkamp tries to attain some sort of unity; Esaias has recourse to this expedient in his drawing of 1629 (see no. 102). The present landscape, it is true, seems to be an exception in its oldfashioned outlook. When Esaias was keeping to the traditional composition-schemes, his drawings of the same years[1] give a far less outdated impression. We may even assume that in the case of our drawing the artist endeavoured to emulate the accomplishments of his pupil Van Goyen.[2] As he did not master the application of these new ideas we need not be surprised that he fell back upon the old ways of dealing with the problem of open space.

[1] Landscape, sale Huldschinsky, Berlin 3.11.1931, no. 95, signed and dated 1626. Landscape with Christ preaching, Amsterdam, Rijksprentenkabinet, signed and dated 1627. [2] Another indication of this ambition may be the painted landscape in Amsterdam, Rijksmuseum, inv. no. 2453, signed and dated 1629.

102. Esaias van de Velde, *Goose-cutting on a canal in a village* p. 225

DATA: Black chalk, brush and black ink, bistre wash, on white paper 271 x 382 mm. Signed at the foot, to the right: 'E. V. VELDE 1629'. Verso: owner's mark Von Lanna (Lugt 2773) and '560', inscription in Goll's handwriting (see Lugt 2987): '1066'. Watermark no. 39.

LITERATURE: Henkel 1916, p. 338; Hirschmann, p. 403; Leporini, no. 230*; Van Regteren Altena 1931, p. 72; Becker, no. 48*; Bernt II, no. 602*.

EXHIBITIONS: Leiden 1916, no. 94; The Hague 1930, I no. 126; Groningen 1931, no. 130; Groningen 1948, no. 113; Groningen 1952, no. 90; The Hague 1955, no. 52.

PROVENANCE: Sale Van Huls, The Hague 14.5.1736, Port. VV no. 2699 (L. 464); — Sale Feitama, Amsterdam 16.10.1758, Kbk H, no. 50 (L. 1019); Sale Goll van Franckenstein, Amsterdam 1.7.1833, Kbk L no. 33? (L. 13362); Sale Von Mecklenburg, Berlin 4.11.1872, no. 1647 (L. 33417); Sale Von Lanna, Stuttgart 16.5.1910, no. 570; — Sale F. A. v. S., Amsterdam, 11.6.1912, no. 260*; — Collection Hofstede de Groot, inv. no. 503, bequest 1914, no. 64; — Groninger Museum voor Stad en Lande, inv. no. 1931–229.

Several other stylistically comparable drawings, among them a series representing the months of the year,[1] are dated 1629. Our drawing is an excellent example, not only of the character of Esaias' work but also of a certain phase in the development of drawing. Prof. Van Regteren Altena[2] remarks that the drawing 'represents very well the young, realistic painter from Haarlem, matter-of-fact, rich in motifs, without style, and *prime-sautier* as he was.'

Scenes like this are easily fitted into the picture that we have of the life of Dutch burghers in the first decades of the seventeenth century. Involuntarily, we think of the *Boertige Liederen* written by a contemporary of Esaias, Adriaan Brederode. In one of these jocular verses, the poet describes a party of young people, on their way to a village feast where there will be 'goose cutting'. This remarkable game is played here while standing in the stern of a rowing-boat, whereas Brederode speaks of a cart. A curious parallel is that the poet describes the costumes of his personages, some of whom are dressed 'op 't oud fatsoen', i.e. in the old fashioned style,

Fig. 31. Hans Bol, *Goose-cutting*. Engraving

with a great variety of colours; others, however, donned the more up-to-date brown velvet. The two couples, fully depicted to the right of the scene, are in fact wearing costumes belonging to different generations.

There are a number of contemporary representations of the same subject. The prototype seems to be an engraving by Hans Bol (fig. 31), who also made a gouache of the goose-cutting at the Hofvijver in The Hague.[3] Our drawing is derived from the engraved composition, with considerable modification. The point of view is lower and the multitude of houses and on-lookers has been reduced so that a clarity of arrangement has been achieved. Jan Savery also used Bol's print for an engraving. The boy, clutching at the goose is—in reverse—the same on both prints. Willem Swanenburgh[4] engraved a design by David Vinckboons in which the moralizing criticism does not seem to be directed against the goose-cutting, there done on horseback, but against the debauchery that apparently went in hand with any *fête villageoise*. P. Molijn also made a drawing of the same theme: sale Robinson and Chennevières, Amsterdam 20.11.1882, no. 137, from the coll. of Sir Thomas Lawrence, present whereabouts unknown.

Van de Velde omitted in this and in most of his later works the very crude and coarse jokes that we find in the work—both pictorial and literary—of his contemporaries from Haarlem and Amsterdam; he worked at the court in The Hague, where a more conservative and formal atmosphere was maintained. Also the onlookers are townspeople rather than country-folk. The artists of the generation of Esaias van de Velde had the habit[5] of depicting the princes and princesses of The Hague court with their noble guests from the Pfaltz at the feasts of commoners. In our drawing we sense the influence of this image. A painting[6] with the same subject, showing some congruence in the composition, may have been painted in the atelier of Esaias van de Velde.

[1] Now in various collections, a.o. Amsterdam, Rijksprentenkabinet, inv. no. A95; British Museum, cat. Hind IV, no. 3; coll. E. Perman, Stockholm, exh. Stockholm, Nationalmuseum, 1953, no. 119. [2] See Bibliography Van Regteren Altena 1931. [3] Copenhagen, Statens Museum for Kunst, catalogue 1922, no. 93; signed and dated 1589. [4] Le Blanc no. 39. [5] Cf. Hendrik Averkamp's drawing of the 'Winterkoning' on the ice, Haarlem, Teyler's Museum, cat. 1904, no. 0*8, Welcker no. T46*. [6] Collection C. J. H. Dierkauf, Utrecht (1959).

103. Willem van de Velde, the Elder, *An English Royal yacht and other vessels in a fresh breeze off the coast* p. 226

DATA: Black chalk, grey wash, on white paper 284 x 494 mm, consisting of two pieces, glued together. Recto, lower right corner: owner's mark W. Mayor (Lugt 2799). Verso: unidentified owner's mark (Lugt 2766), owner's mark John Macgowan (Lugt 1496). Watermark (on both pieces of paper) no. 40.

EXHIBITIONS: The Hague 1930, I no. 127; Groningen 1931, no. 131; Groningen 1952, no. 92; The Hague 1955, no. 54.

PROVENANCE: Sale Macgowan, London 26.1.1804, no. 2 (L. 6733); Coll. W. Mayor, cat. 1875, no. 681; Sale Von Heyl zu Herrnsheim, Stuttgart 25.5.1903, no. 316; — Collection Hofstede de Groot, inv. no. 220, bequest 1914, no. 65; — Groninger Museum voor Stad en Lande, inv. no. 1931–230.

On the right, a royal yacht at anchor, a boat approaching her astern. To the left, a small ketch and a frigate running before the wind.

The collectionmark in verso, a light green crown, listed in Lugt (no. 2766) as unidentified, could possibly be a misprint of the Von Heyl zu Herrnsheim mark (L. 2879) from whose collection the drawing was bought by Hofstede de Groot. The traditional attribution to Willem van de Velde the younger is not correct. The style seems to belong rather to the work of the father. The scene may show shipping in the Thames[1] or Medway, but there were many oc-

104. Willem van de Velde, the Younger, *Shipping in a Mediterranean harbour*

casions when Van de Velde could have drawn a scene such as this. The drawing may belong to one of the large series such as the one illustrating the King's visit to the *Tiger* in 1681.

[¹] Most of the data and the technical descriptions relating to the drawings by or after Willem van der Velde (father and son) we owe to the kind cooperation of Mr. M. S. Robinson of the National Maritime Museum, Greenwich.

104. Willem van de Velde, the Younger, *Shipping in a Mediterranean harbour* p. 124

DATA: Pen and black ink, grey wash, on white paper 142 x 205 mm. Verso: owner's mark Roupell (Lugt 2234).
LITERATURE: Hirschmann, p. 211; Becker, no. 49.
EXHIBITIONS: Leiden 1916C, no. 108; The Hague 1930, I no. 129; Groningen 1931, no. 133; Groningen 1952, no. 91.
PROVENANCE: Sale Roupell, London 23.2.1855, no. ? (L. 22271); Art dealer Dunthorne, London 1909; — Collection Hofstede de Groot, inv. no. 440, bequest 1914, no. 67; — Groninger Museum voor Stad en Lande, inv. no. 1931–232.

To the left, a stern view probably of a Dutch flagship; close astern of her a galley; to the right another galley and on the extreme left, the after part of a third galley. There exist several other drawings¹ which make it seem reasonable to suppose that Van de Velde went to the Mediterranean in 1694. There is no definite proof, on the other hand, that the drawings were done from life.

[¹] Lille, Musée Wicar, inv. no. 1047, photograph Corpus Gernsheim no. 18528. Berlin, Kupferstichkabinett, cat. 1930, no. 5722*, Bernt II, no. 610, Van Gelder, no. 132.

105. Willem van de Velde, the Younger, *Page of a sketch-book with perspective studies and instructions* p. 227

DATA: Pen and bistre, on white paper 189 x 304 mm. Signed in the lower right corner: 'W V V J 1694'.
LITERATURE: Hirschmann, p. 211.
EXHIBITIONS: Groningen 1915, no. 41; Leiden 1916C, no. 109; The Hague 1930, I no. 128; Groningen 1931, no. 132.
PROVENANCE: Sale Duval, Amsterdam 12.6.1910, no. 421; — Collection Hofstede de Groot, inv. no. 439, bequest 1914, no. 66; — Groninger Museum voor Stad en Lande, inv. no. 1931–231.

In the collection of F. Lugt¹ there is another drawing with written explanations, like our drawing probably for the guidance of a pupil, showing the same characteristic hand. Also the signature is beyond any doubt. A transcription of the ms. in the present drawing reads as follows:
'Wint
wint — k konsidereert . hier neu tussen beijde op d disstansi, sult/desse aen notisie vinde

in de schesse naert leeven, want/het oogh bereijckt soo veel het donlijck is, hier/valt dan vrij wat op te lette, dat het hoeft niet/te veel naer de een ofte andere sijde keert, indien/het te ver gaet maeckt van d een twee stucke, om bij den regel/te blijve vant o ogh. W. V. V J 1694.'

The upper row of ships obviously indicates the change in appearance when a ship is moving from a position directly in front of the spectator away towards the right. The lower sketch will be the 'schesse naert leeven'[2] mentioned in the text. The essence of Van de Velde's advice seems to be that the composition is spoiled when the scene is turned too far one way or the other. In other words: the point of view should not be situated too far to the side, as is indicated by the point o.

[1] Inv. no. 63, dated 1704.   [2] I.e. after nature.

106. Imitator of Willem van de Velde, the Younger (Samuel Scott?), *English shipping becalmed off a low coast* p. 228

DATA: Pen and bistre, on brownish paper 119 x 195 mm. Recto, lower right corner: owner's mark Reveley (Lugt 1356).

EXHIBITIONS: Groningen 1915, no. 42; The Hague 1930, I no. 130; Groningen 1931, no. 134.

PROVENANCE: Sale Reveley, London 11.5.1852, no.? (L. 20822); Art dealer Dunthorne, London 1909; — Collection Hofstede de Groot, inv. no. 441, bequest 1914, no. 68; — Groninger Museum voor Stad en Lande, inv. no. 1931–233.

On the right, a ship at anchor; in the left middle-distance, two other ships at anchor; several small vessels and boats under way. In the ship on the right the drawing of the stern is muddled, the fore yard is shown on the wrong side of the mast and rigging and the pendant at the main has been made much too large.[1] In view of this lack of accuracy and facility of drawing the present sketch cannot be accepted as a Willem van de Velde, though in the Ingram collection of Van de Velde drawings[2] there are quite a number of pen and ink sketches, drawn in the same weary manner. Also in the National Maritime Museum there is an album of drawings, which had as frontispiece a mezzotint portrait of Samuel Scott. In this album there are several drawings which relate to known paintings by him and there is little doubt that all the drawings in the album are by Scott. Our sketch bears stylistic resemblance to these drawings so that it is attributed provisionally to Samuel Scott.

[1] For the description, technical data and present attribution we are greatly indebted to Mr. M. S. Robinson, National Maritime Museum, Greenwich.   [2] National Maritime Museum, Greenwich, for instance no. 206.

107, 108, 109, 110. Adriaan van de Venne, *The four seasons* p. 229

DATA: Pen and bistre, grey wash, on brownish paper diameter 120 mm. Signed at the foot: 'A. v. Venne 1624'. Verso: owner's mark R. von Liphart (Lugt 1758) and '886 a–d,'; inscriptions in Goll's handwriting (see Lugt 2987): 'No. 1493–1496'. Watermark no. 41 (upper part on no. 110, lower part on no. 109).

LITERATURE: Henkel 1916, p. 338–39; Hirschmann, p. 404; Bol 1958, p. 59.

EXHIBITIONS: The Hague 1902, no. 145; Leiden 1903, no. 76; Groningen 1915, nos. 43–46; Leiden 1916A, nos. 97–100; The Hague 1930, I nos 131–134; Groningen 1931, nos. 135–138; The Hague 1955, no. 55; Groningen 1952, no. 93.

PROVENANCE: Sale Goll van Franckenstein, Amsterdam 1.7.1833, Omslag VV no. 4 or 5 (L. 13362); Sale Von Liphart, Leipzig 26.4.1898, no. 970 (L. 56238); — Collection Hofstede de Groot, inv. nos. 65–68, bequest 1914, nos. 69–72; — Groninger Museum voor Stad en Lande, inv. nos. 1931–234, 1931–235, 1931–236, 1931–237.

Fig. 32. Adriaan van de Venne, *Sailing boat*. Drawing, Althorp House, Northamptonshire, coll. Earl Spencer.

The four seasons is a subject that suited Van de Venne's 'renaissance-like pleasure in the abundance of realities' (Bol 1958, p. 128). The artist is still tied to the allegorical and historical way of thinking of the preceding generations, doubtless a distant echo of the cyclical contemplation of life of the Middle-Ages. In this regard he is the pictorial counterpart of the well-known popular poet Jacob Cats, whose works he illustrated. Of the figures which people Van de Venne's paintings and drawings, Bol writes that 'their busy or watching presence is determined by the historical or allegorical environment of which they form a part' (Bol 1958, p. 128).

The position which Van de Venne occupies in the cultural development of his country corresponds exactly with his stylistic situation. He follows 'the traditional Flemish composition-principles, but distinguishes himself by a greater sense of reality in his lines and colours ... More than depicting the earth as pure landscape, however, he wanted to narrate the earthly life in his paintings' (Bol 1958, p. 62).

The sailing boat of the drawing with the wooden bridge (no. 108) is also found on p. 41 of the sketchbook in the possession of Earl Spencer, Althorp, Northamptonshire (see fig. 32).

III. Adriaan Verboom, *Old tree near a pool* p. 230

DATA: Pen and bistre, on white paper 142 x 186 mm.

LITERATURE: Henkel 1916, p. 342; Hirschmann, p. 405*; Gerson 1940, no. B22*.

EXHIBITIONS: Groningen 1915, no. 21; Leiden 1916A, no. 14; The Hague 1930, I no. 31; Groningen 1931, no. 37; Groningen 1948, no. 88; Groningen 1952, no. 9.

PROVENANCE: Art dealer Van Gogh, 1901; — Collection Hofstede de Groot, inv. no. 108, bequest 1914, no. 11; — Groninger Museum voor Stad en Lande, inv. no. 1931–136.
See text of the next entry.

112. Adriaan Verboom, *Sheds on a country-road* p. 231

DATA: Pen and bistre, on white paper 150 x 192 mm. Verso, in HdG's handwriting: 'Beeren-steijn'. Owner's mark Hofstede de Groot (L 561).
LITERATURE: Henkel 1916, p. 342; Hirschmann, p. 405; Gerson 1940, no. B23.
EXHIBITIONS: The Hague 1902, no. 1; Groningen 1915, no. 20; Leiden 1916A, no. 15; The Hague 1930, I no. 30; Groningen 1931, no. 36; The Hague 1955, no. 12.
PROVENANCE: Sale Della Faille Waerloos, Amsterdam 19.1.1904, no. 21; — Sale H. Duval a.o., Amsterdam 22.6.1910, no. 25; — Collection Hofstede de Groot, inv. no. 371, bequest 1914, no. 10; — Groninger Museum voor Stad en Lande, inv. no. 1931–135.

These wooded landscapes have up to now been attributed to Beresteyn, together with a large group of drawings by the same hand in various other collections.[1] When studying the documented oeuvre[2] of Nicolaes Beresteyn, we come to see this artist as a mediocre draughts-man, which is not at variance with the fact that he was an amateur. His work bears the stamp of smallness, characteristic of the dilettante. His sometimes enchanting and romantic views of forests have no depth, only hesitantly penetrate into space, and his trees lack real volume. We do not feel as if we were standing on solid soil; this is not so much owing to Beresteyn's skill in rendering a fairy-like atmosphere as simply to lack of visual power. We can add to the small number of documented works only two other drawings by Beresteyn.[3] The present landscapes show too vigorous a hand for the artist to have executed them. We notice a certain romanticism here, it is true; this romanticism however, is of a more powerful nature than that of Beresteyn's works.

Most of the drawings of the group to which our landscapes belong are occasionally credited to Cornelis Vroom or Adriaan Verboom, by scholars who likewise deny the probability of Beresteyn's authorship. We follow the first possibility that Frits Lugt advanced in his catalogue of the Louvre-drawings,[4] since there are three drawings that make an attribution to Verboom plausible. The first is a drawing in Rotterdam[5] where we see in the right foreground the same use of the pen as can be observed in our landscapes. The rest of the drawing resembles the well-known prosaic landscapes that we associate in the first place with the name of Verboom.[6] In Boerner's *Neue Lagerliste* no. 38, 1964, there is also a wooded landscape[7] showing a synthesis of the two manners. The third example is in Berlin,[8] bearing the signature 'A. VBoom f.', closely resembling the present two drawings. There are a few dated etchings[9] by Jacob van Ruisdael that could have been a source of inspiration for Verboom, and in the last half of the forties, Ruisdael also started to produce paintings. It is almost certain that the contact with Ruisdael's work resulted in a strong influence upon Verboom which stimulated him to execute the series of heroic wooded landscapes of which the present drawings are very good examples.

[1] H. Gerson attributed practically all the drawings of this group to Nicolaes Beresteyn in his monography on the artist, inserted as appendix II of *Genealogie van het geslacht Van Beresteyn*, 's-Gravenhage 1940. [2] The etchings 1–9, described in Gerson 1940. Drawing formerly in the collection of Jhr. E. A. van Beresteyn, signed 'C VB', Gerson 1940, no. B21; Drawing in Weimar, Schlossmuseum, signed 'C VB', Gerson 1940, no. B32. [3] Coll.

Van Regteren Altena, Gerson 1940, no. B5; London, British Museum, Cat. Hind, p. 36, no. 1, Gerson 1940, no. B24. [⁴] Lugt, 1929–33, p. 55: '… Restent deux possibilités: (1) Adriaan Hendriksz. Verboom (Rotterdam vers 1628–1670 Amsterdam), que nous connaissons mieux par ses paysages dessinées au lavis d'encre de Chine dans le goût de Jacob van Ruisdael dans sa periode de 1660–70, aurait eu une première manière révélée par ses eaux-fortes et par les dessins à la plume du genre Vroom, correspondant peut-être à son séjour à Harlem entre 1650–60; (2) il y aurait eu un autre Verboom sur lequel manquent les données biographiques.' [⁵] Museum Boymans-van Beuningen, inv. no. AHVI, signed A. H. Verboom. [⁶] Two drawings in the Printroom of the Rijksmuseum, Amsterdam, inv. nos. A125 and '31:61, both signed. Paris, coll. Dutuit, Lugt 1927, no. 85*, signed. Two drawings in the Kunsthalle, Hamburg, inv. no. 22632 and 22633 (Photographs Gernsheim 17724 and 17725), both signed. [⁷] Signed 'VBoom f 1652'. [⁸] Kupferstichkabinett, cat. 1930, no. 6708. [⁹] Le Blanc 6 (1646) and 10 (1647). The theme of the old tree near a pool also occurs in an etching by Ruysdael with a similar emotional content (see: M. E. Dutuit, *Manuel de l'amateur d'estampes, Ecoles Flamande et Hollandaise,* T.3, Paris/Londres, 1885, p. 280, no. 4).

113. Cornelis Visscher, *Portrait of a painter?* p. 232

DATA: Black chalk, on vellum 323 x 255 mm. Signed in the upper right corner: 'C de Visscher fecit'. Pasted on paper.
LITERATURE: De Vries Lam*; Henkel 1916, p. 342; Hirschmann, p. 410; Becker, *Neue Folge,* no. 40.
EXHIBITIONS: Leiden 1916A, no. 106; The Hague 1930, I no. 136; Groningen 1931, no. 140.
PROVENANCE: Art dealer Strölin, Paris 1907; — Collection Hofstede de Groot, inv. no. 302, bequest 1914, no. 74; — Groninger Museum voor Stad en Lande, inv. no. 1931–239.

Two other versions of this portrait[1] exist. The signature and quality of the present drawing indicate that we are dealing with the original. The fact that the appearance of the sitter seems extremely familiar is probably owing to the traditional conception of the portrait and the stereotyped gesture of the sitter. The woodenness of the right fore-arm elicited from Prof. Reznicek the remark that the artist might have used one of the model-books for gestures; the way in which the man presents himself is the same as in Karel Dujardin's painted self-portrait[2] of 1662. We would not be surprised if the sitter were an artist; we did not find sufficient documented material to verify the traditional identification with the painter Jan Wouwerman. The portrait can be dated ca. 1660.

[1] (1) Leiden, Printroom of the University, inv. no. 3643; 352 x 284 mm; not signed. (2) Amsterdam, Rijksprentenkabinet, inv. no. A4019, 310 x 245 mm, not signed, in verso, in a later hand: 'Portrait de Philips Wouwerman par C. de Visscher.' [2] Amsterdam, Rijksmuseum, cat. 1943, no. 827.

114. Cornelis Visscher?, *Portrait of the painter Adam van Oort?* p. 233

DATA: Black chalk, on vellum 163 x 125 mm. Verso: owner's mark Von Heyl zu Herrnsheim (Lugt 2879).
LITERATURE: Hirschmann, p. 410.
EXHIBITIONS: Leiden 1903, no. 85; Leiden 1916A, no. 105; The Hague 1930, I no. 135; Groningen 1931, no. 139; Groningen 1952, no. 95.
PROVENANCE: Sale Von Heyl zu Herrnsheim, Stuttgart 25.5.1903, no. 323; — Collection Hofstede de Groot, inv. no. 221, bequest 1914, no. 73; — Groninger Museum voor Stad en Lande, inv. no. 1931–238.

Probably the drawing is a portrait of the painter Adam van Oort.[1] The traditional, incorrect identification of Abraham Ortelius could only be explained by the similarity of the two names in the latinized version.

There exists a number of portraits of old men, showing a strong general similarity, as if all the different sitters were represented according to a fixed type. Rembrandt painted the

Fig. 33. Anthonie van Dyck, *Portrait of Frans Francken.* Etching
Fig. 34. Hendrick Snyers, *Portrait of Adam van Oort.* Engraving

clergyman Eleazar Swalmius,[2] whose colleague and brother Hendrick was portrayed by Frans Hals.[3] Three individuals, the man in our portrait and the two brothers Swalmius, have been depicted with astonishing conformity. The prototype for this image is found in Rubens's and Van Dyck's portraits of the painter Frans Francken the Elder.[4] In spite of the individual, obviously differing features of all these persons, we are each time confronted apparently with the same, kind old man. As the limits within which the mental and physical appearance of the sitter could be expressed allowed the use of a previously set dominant image, the *vis superba formae* of Van Dyck's popular engraving did not fail to produce its effect in the case of our portrait.

The traditional attribution to Cornelis Visscher is not supported by any convincing evidence.

[1] See the engraved portrait of Van Oort after a painting by Jacob Jordaens, in Cornelis de Bie's *Gulden Cabinet vande edel vry Schilder-const,* etc., Antwerpen, 1661, p. 37, by Hendrick Snyers, Le Blanc no. 2 (see fig. 34). [2] Signed and dated 1637, Hofstede de Groot 1907–28, no. 722, Antwerp, Koninklijk Museum voor Schone Kunsten, exh. Amsterdam 1956, no. 31*. [3] Signed and dated 1639. Hofstede de Groot 1907–28, no. 228, Detroit, The Detroit Institute of Arts, exh. Haarlem 1962, no. 42*. [4] Rubens's portrait in various versions: Montpellier, Musée Fabre, cat. 1926, no. 276. Frankfurt am Main, Städelsches Institut, cat. 1924, no. 640. Van Dyck portrayed Francken in a painting, New York, Metropolitain Museum, and in an etching, Wurzbach 6, Le Blanc 7 (see fig. 33).

115. Simon de Vlieger, *Landscape with trees to the left, to the right a village in a valley* p. 234

DATA: Black chalk, grey wash, on white paper 181 x 275 mm. Signed in the lower left corner: 'S DE VL'; recto, lower left corner: owner's mark Habich (Lugt 862).

LITERATURE: Henkel 1916, p. 342; Hirschmann, p. 405.

EXHIBITIONS: Leiden 1903, no. 79; Leiden 1916A, no. 108; The Hague 1930, I no. 138; Groningen 1931, no. 142; The Hague 1955, no. 57.

PROVENANCE: Collection Miss James; Sale Habich, Stuttgart 27.4.1899, no. 722 (L. 57164); — Art dealer Colnaghi, London 1913; — Collection Hofstede de Groot, inv. no. 195, bequest 1914, no. 76; — Groninger Museum voor Stad en Lande, inv. no. 1931–241.

This drawing can be compared with several documented works by Simon de Vlieger which show the same construction of the landscape. The etching Bartsch no. 3, a signed painting in Rotterdam, Museum Boymans-van Beuningen (cat. 1962, N1924) and a drawing in Berlin, Kupferstichkabinett (cat. 1930, no. 5751) share with our drawing a view in the distance with a river to the right, while from the left foreground a road disappears into a forest which occupies the left half of the picture.

The technique, reminding us of Waterloo's blurred black chalkdrawings, is also found in two drawings with a monogram in Amsterdam, Rijksprentenkabinet (inv. no. A36) and Museum Fodor (inv. no. 249). In Hamburg, Kunsthalle, there are also three drawings (inv. nos. 22656–8) which are in this respect similar to our drawing. We cannot share Mr. Hirschmann's opinion (see Bibliography) that Rembrandt's influence is apparent in the atmospheric effect of De Vlieger's drawing. Especially in the painting in Rotterdam, but also in our drawing, De Vlieger's admiration for the heroic landscape betrays itself more than anything else. However romantic some of Rembrandt's landscapes may be, the heroic landscape, with Jacob Ruisdael as its chief exponent, is of quite another nature.

116. Jan Gerard Waldorp, *Portrait of an old lady seated* p. 235

DATA: Black chalk on vellum 316 x 252 mm.

LITERATURE: Henkel 1916, p. 342; Hirschmann, p. 410; Becker, no. 50*.

EXHIBITIONS: Leiden 1916A, no. 107; The Hague 1930, I no. 137; Groningen 1931, no. 141; Groningen 1952, no. 94; The Hague 1955, no. 56.

PROVENANCE: Sale H. Duval, Amsterdam 22.6.1910, no. 441; — Collection Hofstede de Groot, inv. no. 447, bequest 1914, no. 75; — Groninger Museum voor Stad en Lande, inv. no. 1931–240.

Several artists of the last half of the eighteenth century used to copy their great predecessors of the seventeenth century. Abraham Delfos, Wybrand Hendriks, Cornelis van Noorde and Jan Gerard Waldorp, to name a few of them, had taken to this form of admiration; above all others, the painted portraits of Frans Hals were assiduously copied. The present drawing, which up to now has been considered as the work of Cornelis Visscher, can safely be attributed to Jan Gerard Waldorp.[1] When we compare the portrait with other documented works of this draughtsman, little doubt is left about this new attribution.[2]

It is interesting to note that in this case Waldorp probably copied a certain type of portrait rather than a special painting. The possibility remains that he has been imitating a lost or unknown portrait. As, however, the signature (see note 2) occuring on most of his drawings and indicating that he copied Hals, is lacking, we may assume that Waldorp executed here an original portrait in the style of the middle of the seventeenth century. Hals's Maritge Voogt Claesdochter, and Sara Andriesdochter Hessix, followed by Bol's Elisabeth Bas and Rembrandt's Françoise van Wassenhoven, reveal the coming into existence of a certain type in Dutch portraiture. Waldorp's portrait shows clearly the influence of this image, and in this way the painter indicated that he regarded this era as having passed into history. It is often held that the interest that the nineteenth century took in Holland's Golden Age had the aspect of a sudden revival. Waldorp's approach, with its distinct historical flavour, is an indication that the prestige of this era has its roots in the eighteenth century. The numerous 'genootschappen'[3] with their penchant for historical thinking may have stimulated this development.

[1] Prof. Van Regteren Altena proposed the attribution to Waldorp for the first time. [2] Portrait of a woman, copy after a lost original, companion piece to the 'Man with the thistle' from the coll. Huldschinsky, Hofstede de Groot, 1907–28 no. 258; signed 'F Hals pinx. 1644 J. G. Waldorp del. 1779', present whereabouts unknown, photograph Rijksbureau voor Kunsthistorische Documentatie, The Hague. Portrait of two children, Berlin, Kupferstichkabinett, 2. Garnitur, signed 'F Hals pinx. J. G. Waldorp del. 1782', after a portrait in a private collection, Brussels. Portrait of a woman, Amsterdam, Rijksprentenkabinet, inv. no. '10:30, black chalk on vellum, signed 'F. Hals pix. 1643, J. G. Waldorp del. 1780', after the painting Hofstede de Groot 1907–28, no. 402. [3] Societies with a cultural or scientific aim, founded and flourishing in the last half of the eighteenth century, *mutatis mutandis* comparable to the English 'learned societies'.

117. Anthonie Waterloo, *View of the 'Valkhof' near Nijmegen*　　　p. 236

DATA: Black chalk, grey wash, on white paper 330 x 470 mm. Verso: owners' mark Von Heyl zu Herrnsheim (Lugt 2879). Watermark no. 42.

LITERATURE: Sliepenbeek, p. 64*.

EXHIBITIONS: Leiden 1916C, no. 112; The Hague 1930, I no. 139; Groningen 1931, no. 143; Groningen 1952, no. 96; The Hague 1955, no. 58.

PROVENANCE: Sale Von Heyl zu Herrnsheim, Stuttgart 25.5.1903, no. 330; — Collection Hofstede de Groot, inv. no. 222, bequest 1914, no. 77; — Groninger Museum voor Stad en Lande, inv. no. 1931–242.

One of the many drawings which Waterloo made of the same neighbourhood. The small book on the Valkhof by P. Sliepenbeek (see Bibliography Sliepenbeek) reproducing our drawing, does not enter into a detailed description of the scene. The title of the illustration reads: 'View on the Valkhof to the left. To the right a town. Ca. 1665.' It seems to us that Waterloo made free use of various elements, not necessarily related to one another. One of Waterloo's other representations of the Valkhof bears the date of 1670.[1]

[1] Coll. F. Lugt, Paris, inv. no. 1907, View of the Valkhof. Attributed to Waterloo. Inscribed: ''t hof binnen Nijmegen 1670'. 342 x 465 mm.

THE PLATES

6. Cornelis Bega, *Study of a seated woman*

4. David Bailly, *Portrait of Reyer Pouwelsz. van Reygersberch*

5. David Bailly, *Portrait of Aeltgen Cornelisdr. van Onderwater*

7. Cornelis Bega, *Study of a seated woman*

9. Job Berckheyde?, *Standing soldier*

11. Jan de Bisschop, *Study of two women peeling apples*

12. Anthonie van Borssum?, *Landing-stage and a pollard willow*

13. Leendert van der Cooghen, *Study of the head of a boy*

14. Albert Cuyp, *Landscape near Calcar, with the Monterenberg in the distance*

143

15. Albert Cuyp, *View of a wide landscape*

16. Albert Cuyp, *Study of a reclining shepherd boy*

17. Albert Cuyp, *Study of a cow*

18. Copy after Albert Cuyp, *Studies of a cow and a calf*

147

19. Lambert Doomer, *Wicket in a fence*

20. Egbert van Drielst, *View in the woodland of Eext*

21. Cornelis Dusart, *The feast of St. Nikolaas*

25. Jacques de Gheyn II, *Portrait in miniature of George Clifford, third Earl of Cumberland*

23. Contre-épreuve after Allaert van Everdingen, *Northern landscape*

24. Contre-épreuve after Allaert van Everdingen, *Northern landscape*

27. Jacques de Gheyn II, *Drinking fisherman, sitting on a basket*

28. Jan van Goyen, *Dune landscape with four travellers near a tree*

29. Jan van Goyen, *Anglers on a high bridge*

30. Jan van Goyen, *View on a river with a ruined church*

31. Jan van Goyen, *Seashore with boats and carts*

32. Jan van Goyen?, *Old town on a river*

33. Copy after Jan van Goyen, *Landscape with travellers in front of an inn*

34. Copy after Jan van Goyen, *A canal in a town with a watermill and an arched bridge*

35. Jan Hackaert, *Italian landscape*

36. Nicolaes van Haeften?, *Sheet of studies with twenty-one sketches*

37. Hendrik Johan Haverman, *Portrait of the painter Jacob Maris*

40. Jacob Koninck?, *Farmhouse by the waterside*

38, 39. Guilliam de Heer, *Wedding-portraits of Johannes Bogaert and Maria Wijnands*

Ætatis Sua 33
1634

167

41. Philips Koninck, *View over a wide landscape near Haarlem*

42. Philips Koninck, *Head of a peasant*

43. Philips Koninck, *Study of three heads*

44. Philips Koninck?, *Farmhouse in a hilly landscape*

45. Jan Lievens, *Portrait of William Kerr, third Earl of Lothian*

46. Jan Lievens, *Portrait of René Descartes*

47. Jan Lievens, *View on a town, to the left a high tree*

174

48. Copy after Jan Lievens, *The roller-bridge to the Sloterpolder near Amsterdam*

49. Copy after Jan Lievens, *View of a small bridge and a farm-house surrounded by trees*

50. Nicolaes Maes?, *Two studies of Titus van Rijn, Rembrandt's son*

51. Pieter Molijn, *Winter landscape*

53. Pieter Mulier, the Younger (Cavaliere Tempesta), *Old house with climber*

54. Chrispijn van de Passe, *Cat, mouse and a lizard*

55. Rembrandt, *Old man, facing to the left*

56. Rembrandt, *Actor in the character of Pantalone*

182

57. Rembrandt, *Saskia sitting up in bed*

58. Rembrandt, *Woman lying in bed, and a nurse*

59. Rembrandt, *Isaac blessing Jacob*

61. Rembrandt, *Scene from the Old Testament*

186

62. Rembrandt, *The daughters of Cecrops finding Erichthoneus*

63. Rembrandt, *The departure of the prodigal son*

64. Rembrandt, *Study of a standing woman and the heads of two men*

65. Rembrandt, *Farm-house with a clump of trees to the right*

190

66. Rembrandt, *An Oriental, standing*

67. Rembrandt, *Landscape with farm-house and a rolling horse*

192

68. Rembrandt, *Farm-house with a water-mill surrounded by trees*

193

70. Rembrandt, *A small inn and sheds near a group of trees*

71. Rembrandt?, *Striding angel*

72. School of Rembrandt, *Woman kneeling before a bearded old man*

73. School of Rembrandt, *Jacob kneeling in prayer*

74. School of Rembrandt, *The star of the Kings*

75. School of Rembrandt, *Elegant couple*

76. School of Rembrandt, *Daniel in the lion's den*

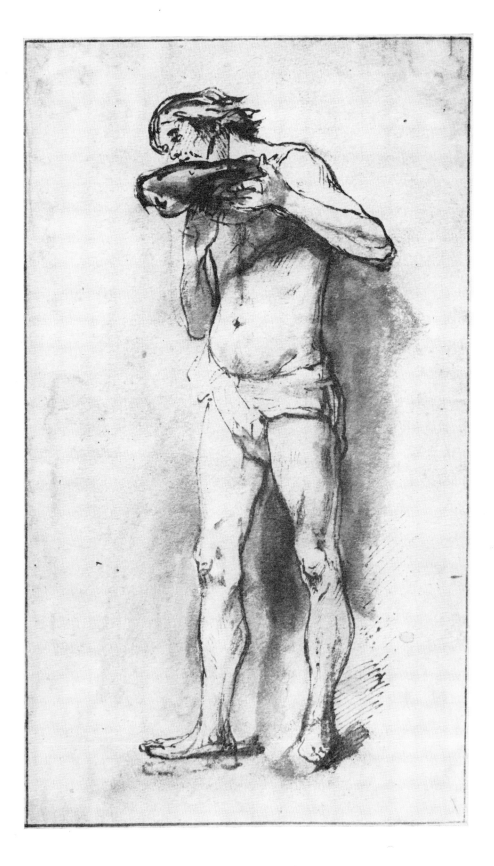

77. School of Rembrandt, *Study of a standing male nude*

78. School of Rembrandt, *Scholar in a room, his right hand resting on a skull*

79. School of Rembrandt, *Oriental descending a hill towards a city*

80. School of Rembrandt (Gerbrand van den Eeckhout?), *Elisha fed by the ravens*

81. School of Rembrandt, *Christ among the doctors*

82. School of Rembrandt, *The Shunamite woman before Elisha at Mount Carmel*

83. Imitator of Rembrandt, *A family in a large interior*

84. Imitator of Rembrandt, *Landscape with a farm-house and a draughtsman*

85. Roeland Roghman, *The Pierre-Pertuis pass*

86. Roeland Roghman, *Landscape with a chapel, a fortified bridge, and a perspective with mountains*

87. Roeland Roghman, *View of the village of Rijnsburg*

88. Roeland Roghman, *The river Amstel near Ouderkerk*

89. Jacob van Ruisdael, *The ruins of the castle of Egmond*

90. Jacob van Ruisdael, *Landscape with sheds on the bank of a canal*

214

91. Cornelis Saftleven, *Woman sitting near a kitchen fire*

92. Cornelis Saftleven, *Standing youth in a long coat*

93. Cornelis Saftleven?, *Sleeping boy*

94. Herman Saftleven, *A dingy at a ship-yard*

95. Herman Saftleven, *Composition with topographical elements of the city of Prague*

96. Michael Sweerts?, *Portrait of a boy*

220

98. Wallerant Vaillant, *Portrait of Dr Jan Bicker*

99. Wallerant Vaillant, *Portrait of Jacob Bicker*

100. Adriaan van de Velde, *Herdsmen and cattle at a watering-place*

101. Esaias van de Velde, *Landscape with gallows*

102. Esaias van de Velde, *Goose-cutting on a canal in a village*

103. Willem van de Velde, the Elder, *An English Royal yacht and other vessels in a fresh breeze off the coast*

105. Willem van de Velde, the Younger, *Page of a sketch-book with perspective studies and instructions*

106. Imitator of Willem van de Velde, the Younger (Samuel Scott?),
English shipping becalmed off a low coast

228

107, 108, 109, 110. Adriaan van de Venne, *The four seasons*

229

III. Adriaan Verboom, *Old tree near a pool*

112. Adriaan Verboom, *Sheds on a country-road*

113. Cornelis Visscher, *Portrait of a painter?*

114. Cornelis Visscher?, *Portrait of the painter Adam van Oort?*

233

115. Simon de Vlieger, *Landscape with trees to the left, to the right a village in a valley*

116. Jan Gerard Waldorp, *Portrait of an old lady seated*

117. Anthonie Waterloo, *View of the 'Valkhof' near Nijmegen*

BIBLIOGRAPHY AND ABBREVIATIONS
LIST OF EXHIBITION CATALOGUES
WATERMARKS
INDEXES

BIBLIOGRAPHY AND ABBREVIATIONS

Auerbach: Erna Auerbach, *Nicholas Hilliard,* London, 1961.

Bartsch: Adam Bartsch, *Le Peintre-graveur,* Vols. I–XXI, Vienne, 1803–1821.

Becker: Felix Becker, *Handzeichnungen Holländischer Meister aus der Sammlung Dr C. Hofstede de Groot im Haag,* Leipzig, 1923.

Becker, *Neue Folge:* —,—, *Neue Folge,* Leipzig, 1923.

Benesch 1935: Otto Benesch, *Rembrandt, Werk und Forschung,* Wien, 1935.

Benesch: Otto Benesch, *The drawings of Rembrandt, first complete edition in six volumes,* I–VI, London, 1954–1957.

Bernt: Walther Bernt, *Die Niederländischen Zeichner des 17. Jahrhunderts,* 2 Vols., München, 1957–1958.

Le Blanc: M. Ch. Le Blanc, *Manuel de l'Amateur d'Estampes contenant le Dictionnaire des Graveurs de toutes les Nations,* Tome I–IV, Paris, 1889.

Von Bode: Wilhelm von Bode, *Frans Hals, sein Leben und seine Werke,* Berlin, 1914.

Bol 1958: L.J.Bol, 'Een Middelburgse Bruegel-groep', I–IX, in *Oud Holland,* LXX(1955)–LXXIV(1959).

Bol 1963: L. J. Bol, *Bekoring van het kleine,* Stichting Openbaar Kunstbezit, 1963.

Brugmans: H. Brugmans, *Geschiedenis van Amsterdam van den oorsprong af tot heden,* Amsterdam, 1930.

Bruyn: J. Bruyn, 'David Bailly', in *Oud Holland,* LXII, 1951, p. 148–164, 212–227.

Catton Rich: D. Catton Rich, 'A double portrait by Sir Thomas Lawrence and the promenade tradition', in *Worcester Art Museum Annual,* Vol. VII, 1959, p. 1–11.

Dattenberg: Heinrich Dattenberg, 'Kalkar und der Monterenberg, Unbekannte Ansichten Holländischer Künstler des 17. Jahrhunderts', in *Sonderveröffentlichung des Heimathauses des Niederrheines in Krefeld,* 14, 1941.

Dessins de Rembrandt: Dessins de Rembrandt, tirés de la collection C. Hofstede de Groot à la Haye, reproduits en facsimile par Emrik & Binger, Haarlem, 1909.

Drost: Willy Drost, *Adam Elsheimer als Zeichner,* Stuttgart, 1957.

Drugulin 1860: W. E. Drugulin, *Allgemeiner Portrait-Katalog. Verzeichnis einer Sammlung von 24000 Portraits berühmter Personen aller Länder und Zeiten,* 2 Bde, Leipzig, 1860.

Drugulin 1873: W. Drugulin, *Allart van Everdingen, Catalogue raisonné de toutes les Estampes qui forment son Œuvre gravé. Supplément au Peintre-graveur de Bartsch,* Leipzig, 1873.

Eisenmann: O. Eisenmann, *Fünfundzwanzig Handzeichnungen alter Meister aus der Sammlung Edward Habich zu Cassel,* Lübeck, 1890.

Franken: D. Franken Dzn., *l'Œuvre gravée des Van de Passe,* Amsterdam/Paris, 1881.

Franken and Van der Kellen: D. Franken Dzn. et J. Ph. van der Kellen, *l'Œuvre de Jan van de Velde,* Amsterdam/Paris, 1883.

Frerichs 1956: [L. C. J. Frerichs], catalogue of the exhibition *De verzameling van Dr A. Welcker,* Amsterdam, Rijksprentenkabinet, 1956.

Frerichs 1959: L. C. J. Frerichs, Radio-lecture for Openbaar Kunstbezit, 1959 no. 33.

Frerichs 1963: L. C. J. Frerichs, *Keuze van tekeningen, Rijksprentenkabinet Amsterdam,* Amsterdam, 1963.

De Gelder: J. J. de Gelder, *Honderd teekeningen van oude meesters in het prentenkabinet der Rijksuniversiteit te Leiden,* Rotterdam, 1920.

H. E. Van Gelder: H. E. van Gelder, *Holland by Dutch artists*, Amsterdam, 1959.

Van Gelder: J. G. van Gelder, *Prenten en tekeningen*, Amsterdam, 1958.

Gerson 1936: Horst Gerson, *Philips Koninck, ein Beitrag zur Erforschung der holländischen Malerei des XVII. Jahrhunderts*, Berlin, 1936.

Gerson 1940: H. Gerson, 'Leven en werken van Claes van Beresteyn', Bijlage II der *Genealogie van het geslacht van Beresteyn*, 's-Gravenhage, 1940.

Göpel: Erhard Göpel, 'Der Sammler Hofstede de Groot', in *Kunst und Künstler* XXIX, Heft V, Februar 1931, p. 195–202.

Gorissen: F. Gorissen, *Conspectus Cliviae, Die klevische Residenz in der Kunst des 17. Jahrhunderts*, Kleve, 1964.

Van der Grinten: E. F. van der Grinten, *Enquiries into the history of art-historical functions and terms up to 1850*, Diss. Litt. 1952–53 no. 4, Municipal University of Amsterdam, Delft, 1952.

Gudlaugsson: S. Gudlaugsson, *De komedianten bij Jan Steen en zijn tijdgenoten*, 's-Gravenhage, 1945.

Haverkamp Begemann: E. Haverkamp Begemann, 'Otto Benesch, the drawings of Rembrandt' etc., in *Kunstchronik*, 1, 2, 3, 1961, p. 10–28, 50–57, 85–91.

Heckscher: W. S. Heckscher, 'Physically present yet mentally absent, ancient art and its echoes in post-classical times', *Imago, a pictorial calender for 1963*. The Netherlands Classical Association, 1963.

Hell: Hans Hell, 'Die späten Handzeichnungen Rembrandts', in *Repertorium für Kunstwissenschaft*, LI, 1930, p. 4–43, 92–136.

Henkel 1916: M. D. Henkel, 'Ausstellung von Handzeichnungen Holländischer Meister aus dem Besitze von Dr C. Hofstede de Groot in der Tuchhalle in Leiden', in *Kunstchronik*, N.F., XXVII, 1915–16, p. 337–343.

Henkel 1931: M. D. Henkel, *Le dessin hollandais des origines au XVIIe siècle*, Paris, 1931.

Henkel 1939: M. D. Henkel, 'Cornelis Troost', in Thieme-Becker, *Allgemeines Lexicon der bildenden Künstler*, XXXIII, Leipzig, 1939, p. 426–427.

Henkel 1942: M. D. Henkel, *Catalogus van Nederlandsche Teekeningen in het Rijksmuseum te Amsterdam*, Deel I, *Teekeningen van Rembrandt en zijn school*, 's-Gravenhage, 1942.

Hirschmann: Otto Hirschmann, 'Die Handzeichnungen-Sammlung Dr Hofstede de Groot im Haag' I, II u. III, in *Der Cicerone*, VIII, 1916, p. 400–410; IX, 1917, p. 6–22, 199–211.

Hofstede de Groot 1906: C. Hofstede de Groot, *Die Handzeichnungen Rembrandts, Versuch eines beschreibenden und kritischen Katalogs*, Haarlem, 1906.

Hofstede de Groot 1907–28: Dr C. Hofstede de Groot, *Beschreibendes und kritisches Verzeichnis der Werke der hervorragendsten Holländischen Maler des XVII. Jahrhunderts*, Vols. I–X, Esslingen/Paris, 1907–1928.

Hofstede de Groot 1914: C. Hofstede de Groot, 'Episcopius, Johannes', in Thieme-Becker, *Allgemeines Lexicon der bildenden Künstler*, X, Leipzig, 1914, p. 581–582.

Hofstede de Groot 1929: C. Hofstede de Groot, 'Einige Betrachtungen über die Ausstellung Holländischer Kunst in London', in *Repertorium für Kunstwissenschaft*, L, 1929, p. 134–146.

Kauffmann: H. Kauffmann, 'Zur Kritik der Rembrandt-Zeichnungen', in *Repertorium für Kunstwissenschaft*, XLVII, 1926, p. 157–178.

Kossmann: E. F. Kossmann, *Nieuwe bijdragen tot de geschiedenis van het Nederlandsche tooneel in de 17e en 18e eeuw*, Den Haag, 1915.

Kruse: John Kruse, *Die Zeichnungen Rembrandts und seiner Schule im National Museum zu Stockholm. Beschreibender und kritischer Katalog. Aus dem Nachlass Kruses herausgegeben von Ca. Neumann in Heidelberg*, Den Haag, 1920.

Lambourne: Nigel Lambourne, *Rembrandt van Rijn, paintings, drawings and etchings*, London, 1963.

Leporini: H. Leporini, *Die Stilenentwicklung der Handzeichnung*, Wien/Leipzig, 1925.

Lippmann-HdG: *Zeichnungen von Rembrandt Harmensz. van Rijn in Lichtdruck nachgebildet, herausgegeben unter der Leitung von F. Lippmann im Verein mit W. Bode, Sidney Colvin, F. Seymour Haden und J. P. Heseltine* (first series) I–IV. Lieferung, Berlin 1881–92.

Original drawings by Rembrandt Harmensz. van Rijn, reproduced in phototype, edited by F. Lippmann, continued by C. Hofstede de Groot, second series, part I–II, London/The Hague, 1900–01.

Original drawings by Rembrandt Harmensz. van Rijn, reproduced in the colours of the originals by C. Hofstede de Groot, third series, part I–II, The Hague, 1903–06.

Original drawings by Rembrandt Harmensz. van Rijn, reproduced in the colours of the originals, edited by C. Hofstede de Groot, fourth series, part I–II, The Hague, 1911–10.

Lot: Germaine Lot, *Descartes*, Paris, 1966.

L.: Frits Lugt, *Répertoire des catologues de ventes publiques intéressant l'art ou la curiosité*, I: 1600–1825, II: 1826–1860, III: 1961–1900, La Haye, 1938–1965.

Lugt: Frits Lugt, *Les marques de collections de dessins et d'estampes*, Amsterdam, 1921 (Supplément, La Haye, 1956).

Lugt 1920: Frits Lugt, *Mit Rembrandt in Amsterdam, die Darstellungen Rembrandts vom Amsterdamer Stadtbilde und von der unmittelbare Landschaftlichen Umgebung*, Berlin, 1920.

Lugt 1929–33: F. Lugt, *Musée du Louvre, inventaire général des dessins des écoles du nord, Ecole Hollandaise*, I–III, Paris 1929–33.

Lugt 1950: Frits Lugt, *Ecole Nationale supérieure des Beaux-Arts, Paris, inventaire général des dessins des écoles du Nord*, Tome I, école hollandaise, Paris, 1950.

Michel: Emile Michel, *Rembrandt, sa vie, son œuvre et son temps*, Paris, 1893.

Moes: E. W. Moes, in *Bulletin Nederlandschen Oudheidkundigen Bond*, II no. 3, januari 1901, p. 146.

Nordström: Johan Nordström, 'Till Cartesius ikonografi', in *Lychnos*, 1957–58, p. 194–250.

Parker: K. T. Parker, 'Rembrandt van Rijn (1606–1667)' in *Old master drawings*, V, 1931, no. 20, p. 73–74.

Poortenaar: Jan Poortenaar, *Rembrandt teekeningen, honderd en vier afbeeldingen met een inleiding en aanteekeningen*, Naarden, z.j.

Van Puyvelde: L. van Puyvelde, *The Dutch drawings in the collection of His Majesty the King at Windsor Castle*, London/New York, 1944.

Van Regteren Altena 1931: J. Q. van Regteren Altena, 'Groningen's Aanwinsten' in *Maandblad voor Beeldende Kunst*, VIII, 1931, p. 67–75.

Van Regteren Altena 1935: J. Q. van Regteren Altena, *Jacques de Gheyn, an introduction to the study of his drawings*, Diss. Amsterdam 5 July 1935. Amsterdam, 1935.

Van Regteren Altena 1948: J. Q. van Regteren Altena, *Holländische Meisterzeichnungen des siebzehnten Jahrhunderts*, Basel, 1948.

Van Regteren Altena 1960: J. Q. van Regteren Altena, Radio-lecture for 'Openbaar Kunstbezit', 1960, no. 38a.

Reznicek: E. K. J. Reznicek, *Die Zeichnungen von Hendrick Goltzius*, 2 Vols., Utrecht, 1961.

Rosenberg 1928: Jakob Rosenberg, *Jacob van Ruisdael*, Berlin, 1928.

Rosenberg 1964: Jacob Rosenberg, *Rembrandt, life and work*, revised edition, London, 1964.

Rotermund: Hans-Martin Rotermund, *Rembrandts Handzeichnungen und Radierungen zur Bibel*, Stuttgart, 1963.

Scheidig: Walther Scheidig, *Rembrandt als Zeichner*, Leipzig, 1962.

Schinnerer: A. Schinnerer, *Rembrandt Zeichnungen*, München, 1944.

Schneider: H. Schneider, *Jan Lievens, sein Leben und seine Werke*, Haarlem, 1932.

Von Seidlitz: W. von Seidlitz, 'Die Sammlung der Rembrandtzeichnungen von Dr. C. Hofstede de Groot im Haag', in *Zeitschrift für Bildende Kunst*, LII (N.F.XXVIII), 1917, p. 246–254.

Von Sick: Ilse von Sick, *Nicolaes Berchem, ein Vorläufer des Rokoko*, Berlin, 1930.

Simon: Kurt Erich Simon, *Jacob von Ruisdael, eine Darstellung seiner Entwicklung*, Berlin, 1930.

Singer: Hans Wolfgang Singer, *Neuer Bildniskatalog*, I–V, Leipzig, 1937–1938.

Sliepenbeek: [P. Sliepenbeek,] *Het Valkhof, historisch Nijmegen in pen en penseel*, Brugge, 1961.

Stechow 1951: Wolfgang Stechow, 'Some portraits by Michael Sweerts', in *The Art Quarterly*, Autumn 1951, p. 206–215.

Stechow 1963: Wolfgang Stechow, 'The finding of Erichthoneus: an ancient theme in Baroque Art', in *Studies in Western Art (Acts of the twentieth international congress of the history of Art)*, Vol. III, Princeton (New Jersey), 1963, p. 27 ff.

Sumowski: Werner Sumowski, *Bemerkungen zu Otto Beneschs Corpus der Rembrandtzeichnungen*, II, Bad Pyrmont, 1961.

Teding van Berkhout: Jhr. H. Teding van Berkhout, *25 teekeningen door Rembrandt uit de verzameling Dr C. Hofstede de Groot*, Amsterdam, 1913.

Timmers: Prof. dr. J. J. M. Timmers, *Symboliek en Iconographie der Christelijke Kunst*, Roermond/Maaseik, 1947.

Valentiner: Wilhelm R. Valentiner, *Rembrandt, des Meisters Handzeichnungen*, I u. II, Klassiker der Kunst 31/32, Berlin/Leipzig, z.j.

Valentiner 1923: W. R. Valentiner, 'Aus Rembrandts Häuslichkeit', in *Jahrbuch für Kunstwissenschaft*, I, 1923, p. 277 ff.

Valentiner 1924: Wilhelm R. Valentiner, *Nicolaes Maes*, Berlin/Leipzig, 1924.

Valentiner 1925–26: Wilhelm R. Valentiner, 'Komödiantendarstellungen Rembrandts', in *Zeitschrift für Bildende Kunst*, LIX, 1925–26, p. 265–277.

Valentiner 1931: W. R. Valentiner, 'Rembrandt drawings in the Havemeyer Collection' in *Metropolitain Museum Studies*, III, 2, June 1931, p. 135–146.

Volskaja: W. Volskaja, 'Teatra personagi v Risunkach Rembrandt', in *Iskusstwo* IV, 1961, p. 54–60.

De Vries Lam: D. de Vries Lam, 'Een belangrijke schenking', in *De Amsterdammer* (weekly magazine) no. 1965, 21 February 1915, p. 6.

Van de Waal: H. van de Waal, 'Rembrandt's Faust etching, a Socinian Document, and the iconography of the inspired scholar', in *Oud Holland*, LXXIX, 1964, 1, p. 6–48.

Weigel 1843: R. Weigel, *Suppléments au Peintre-graveur de A. Bartsch*, Leipzig, 1843.

Weigel 1865: R. Weigel, *Die Werke der Maler in ihren Handzeichnungen. Beschreibendes Verzeichnis der Facsimiles von Originalzeichnungen*, Leipzig, 1865.

Welcker: Clara J. Welcker, *Hendrik Averkamp 1585–1634, bijgenaamd 'de Stomme van Campen' en Barent Averkamp 1612–1679, 'Schilders tot Campen'*, Zwolle, 1933.

Wimmer: Gertrud Wimmer, *Rembrandts Landschaftszeichnungen*. Inaugural-Dissertation, Frankfurt am Main, 1935.

Witkowski: Georg Witkowski, 'Das Amsterdamer Theater und Rembrandt', in *Drie en dertigste Jaarboek van het Genootschap Amstelodamum*, Amsterdam, 1936, p. 97–139.

Wurzbach: Dr. Alfred von Wurzbach, *Niederländisches Künstler-Lexicon*, I–III, Wien/Leipzig, 1906–1911.

LIST OF EXHIBITION CATALOGUES

Amsterdam 1898: *Rembrandt. Collection des Œuvres du Maître réunies à l'Occasion de l'Inauguration de S. M. la Reine Wilhelmine au Musée de la Ville à Amsterdam, 8 Septembre–31 Octobre 1898.*

Amsterdam 1903: *Catalogue des œuvres de Jan van Goyen réunies par M.M. Muller & Cie au Musée Communal de la ville d'Amsterdam, 15 juillet–1 septembre 1903.*

Amsterdam 1906: *Catalogue de l'exposition de Maîtres Hollandais du XVIIe siècle organisé par MM. Frederik Muller & Cie en l'honneur du Tercentenaire de Rembrandt, 10 juillet–15 septembre 1906.*

Amsterdam 1913: *Vereeniging Rembrandt. Tentoonstelling van een zevental schilderijen en van twee en negentig teekeningen door Rembrandt, waaronder vijf en zestig, door Dr C. Hofstede de Groot aan de Staat geschonken, Stedelijk Museum te Amsterdam, 25 Augustus tot 14 September 1913.*

Amsterdam/Rotterdam 1956: *Rembrandt, Tentoonstelling ter Herdenking van de Geboorte van Rembrandt op 15 juli 1606, Museum Boymans Rotterdam 18 Mei–5 Augustus 1956, Rijksmuseum Amsterdam 8 Augustus–21 October 1956.*

Amsterdam 1964: *Bijbelse Inspiratie, Tekeningen en Prenten van Lucas van Leyden en Rembrandt, Rijksmuseum Amsterdam, 18 nov. 1964–8 febr. 1965.*

Breda 1952: *Nassau-Oranje Tentoonstelling, Breda, Huis van Brecht (Koninklijke Militaire Academie), 1952.*

Bruxelles 1961: *Dessins hollandais du siècle d'Or, Choix de Dessins provenant de Collections publiques et particulières Néerlandaises, Bibliothèque Albert Ier, Bruxelles, 22 Avril–24 Juin, 1961.*

Düsseldorf 1953: *Niederrheinansichten Holländischer Künstler des 17. Jahrhunderts, Kunstmuseum Düsseldorf 1953.*

Groningen 1915: *Lijst van Schilderijen en Teekeningen geschonken door Dr P. [sic!] Hofstede de Groot, aanwezig in het Museum van Oudheden te Groningen, Groningen 1915.*

Groningen 1931: *Groningsch Museum, Verzameling Dr C. Hofstede de Groot, Schilderijen en Teekeningen van Nederlandsche Meesters, Hoofdzakelijk uit de 17e Eeuw, geschonken aan de Gemeente Groningen, Maart en April, 1931.*

Groningen 1948: *Oude Meesters, Nieuwe Aanwinsten in het Museum van Oudheden voor de Provincie en Stad Groningen, 23 Oktober t/m 21 November, 1948.*

Groningen 1952: *Honderd Tekeningen, Gronings Museum 1952.*

Den Haag 1902: *Haagsche Kunstkring, Tentoonstelling van Teekeningen van Oude Hollandsche Meesters uit de Verzameling van Dr Corn. Hofstede de Groot. 16 December 1902–2 Januari 1903.*

Den Haag 1930, I: *Verzameling Dr C. Hofstede de Groot, I, Kunstwerken nagelaten aan de Musea te Groningen en Haarlem, Gemeente Museum, ('s-Gravenhage), 7–27 Juni 1930.*

Den Haag 1955: *Keuze van Schilderijen en Tekeningen uit de Verzameling C. Hofstede de Groot nagelaten aan de Gemeente Groningen, Rijksbureau voor Kunsthistorische Documentatie, April 1955.*

Haarlem 1951: *Rembrandt Tentoonstelling, Tekeningen en Etsen, Haarlem, Vleeshal, 2 Juni–3 September 1951.*

Ingelheim 1964: *Holländische Zeichnungen des 17. Jahrhunderts in Ingelheim am Rhein, Ausstellung vom 18.4.–3.5.1964.*

Leiden 1903: *Vereeniging 'Die Laecken-Halle', te Leiden. Tentoonstelling van Teekeningen van Oud-Nederlandsche Meesters, te houden van 7 tot 28 October 1903.*

Leiden 1916 A–C: *Tentoonstelling van Teekeningen van Oud-Hollandsche Meesters uit de Verzameling van Dr C. Hofstede de Groot, Stedelijk Museum 'De Lakenhal', Leiden,*

A, *Teekeningen uit den Tijd vóór Rembrandt en van Meesters, die niet onder Rembrandt's Invloed staan; benevens enkele Gezichten op Kasteelen in de Omgeving van Leiden. 8 Maart–7 April 1916.*

B, *Tentoonstelling in het Stedelijk Museum 'De Lakenhal' te Leiden, van Teekeningen van Rembrandt uit de verzameling van Dr C. Hofstede de Groot. 11 April–10 Mei 1916.*

C, *Tentoonstelling in het Stedelijk Museum 'De Lakenhal' te Leiden, van Teekeningen van Hollandsche Meesters uit de Verzameling van Dr C. Hofstede de Groot. 12 Mei–14 Juni 1916.*

Leiden 1956: *Stedelijk Museum de Lakenhal, Leiden, 1 Juni–1 September 1956, Rembrandt als Leermeester.*

Leiden/Arnhem 1960: *Jan van Goyen, Leiden, Stedelijk Museum 'De Lakenhal', 4 Juni–27 Juli 1960, Arnhem, Gemeentemuseum 31 Juli–26 September 1960.*

Londen 1899: *Exhibition of works by Rembrandt, Winter Exhibition (Royal Academy of Arts in London) MDCCCXCIX.*

London 1964: *The Orange and the Rose, Holland and Britain in the Age of Observation 1600–1750, Victoria and Albert Museum, October 22 to December 13, 1964.*

Paris 1908: *Bibliothèque Nationale, Exposition d'Œuvres de Rembrandt, Dessins et Gravures, Mai–Juin 1908, Catalogue rédigé par François Courboin, Joseph Guibert, P.-André Lemoisne, Paris 1908.*

Paris 1921: *Exposition Hollandaise. Tableaux, Aquarelles et Dessins anciens et modernes, (Paris), Avril–Mai 1921.*

Paris 1960: *Bestiaire Hollandais, Exposition de Tableaux, Aquarelles, Dessins et Gravures par des Artistes Hollandais des XVIIe–XVIIIe Siècles et d'un Choix de Livres de la même Période, 1er–27e Mars 1960, Institut Néerlandais, Paris.*

Paris 1967: *La vie en Hollande au XVIIe siècle, Exposition organisée par l'Institut Néerlandais, Musée des arts décoratifs, Paris 1967.*

Prague 1966: *Tri století nizozemské kresby 1400–1700, Národní Galerie v. Praze, 1966.*

Recklinghausen 1960/61: *Ernte der Synagoga Recklinghausen, Frankfurt am Main, (1962).*

Vancouver 1958: *The changing Landscape of Holland, an Exhibition of Watercolours and Drawings of the Netherlands from 1600 to 1900, The Vancouver International Festival, July 23rd to August 29th 1958, The Fine Arts Gallery, University of British Columbia, Vancouver B.C., Canada.*

Washington 1958/59: *Dutch Drawings, Masterpieces of five Centuries, Exhibition organized by the Printroom of the Rijksmuseum, Amsterdam, and circulated by the Smithsonian Institution, 1958–1959.*

WATERMARKS

1

P B

2

3

4

5

6

7

8

9

10

11

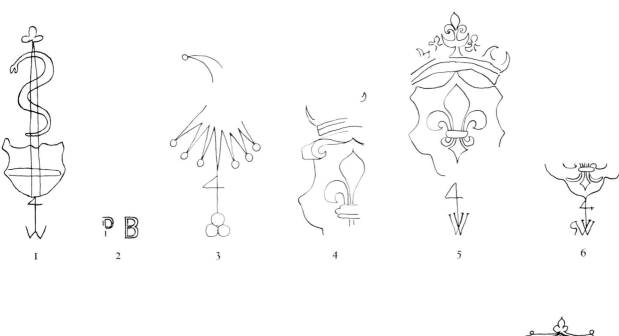

12

MC

13

SW

14

15

WR

16

17

SW

19

IHS

18

20

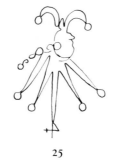

MC

21

PB

22

23

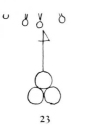

24

25

26

27

246

28

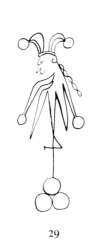

29

30

31

32

33

34

35

36

37

38

39

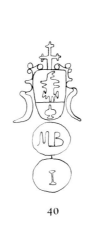

40

41

42

INDEXES

Index of Persons

Numbers in Italics refer to the catalogue entries; numbers in Roman type refer to page numbers.

Topographical Index